HUMAN BODY

An Hachette UK Company
www.hachette.co.uk

First published in Great Britain in 2017 by Bounty Books,
a division of Octopus Publishing Group Ltd
Carmelite House, 50 Victoria Embankment
London EC4Y 0DZ
www.octopusbooks.co.uk

Edited and designed by Anna Bowles and Perfect Bound Ltd

ISBN 978 0 7537 3236 6

Printed and bound in China

10 9 8 7 6 5 4 3 2 1

Publisher: Lucy Pessell
Designer: Lisa Layton
Editor: Natalie Bradley
Proofreader: Jane Birch
Administrative Assistant: Sarah Vaughan
Production Controller: Sarah Kulasek-Boyd

Artworks created by Perfect Bound Ltd

COLOR + LEARN
HUMAN BODY

MORE THAN 200 PAGES OF FASCINATING FACTS + COLORING

Bounty
Books

CONTENTS

Your Body 8

Your Organs 10

PART 1: CONTROL CENTER 12

The Brain 14
Your internal computer

Parts of the Brain 16
Which bit controls what?

Left and Right Brain 18
Lefties and righties

Memory 20
Your internal database

Intelligence 22
It's not about brain size

The Growing Brain 24
How we learn to think

Nerves 26
Signals to the brain

The Nervous System 28
A network of nerves

Sleep 30
Rest for the brain

Dreams 32
The brain at night

PART 2: HEART AND LUNGS 34

What is Blood? 36
The fluid that feeds your organs

The Heart 38
Pumping blood around your body

Red Blood Cells 40
Oxygen-carriers

White Blood Cells 42
Tiny healers

Veins and Arteries 44
Blood vessels

Capillaries 46
The tiniest vessels

The Spleen 48
Filtering the blood

Blood Groups 50
The ABO system

Blood Clotting   52
How wounds stop bleeding

Why Do We Breathe?   54
The need for air

How Do We Breathe?   56
Taking in air

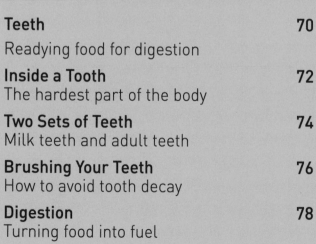

The Mouth   80
Where digestion begins

Saliva   82
Lubricating food

The Throat   84
Breathing and swallowing

Water   86
The basic component of life

Food   88
The essentials to survive

Vitamins   90
Vital chemicals

Food's Journey   92
From mouth to anus

The Stomach   94
Absorbing nutrients

The Intestines   96
Food's onward journey

The Liver   98
Making chemicals

The Lungs   58
Processing air

Inside the Lungs   60
Getting oxygen to the blood

Speech   62
How we talk

Different Voices   64
We all sound different

Speech Without Speaking   66
Body language

PART 3: EATING AND DIGESTION 68

Teeth   70
Readying food for digestion

Inside a Tooth   72
The hardest part of the body

Two Sets of Teeth   74
Milk teeth and adult teeth

Brushing Your Teeth   76
How to avoid tooth decay

Digestion   78
Turning food into fuel

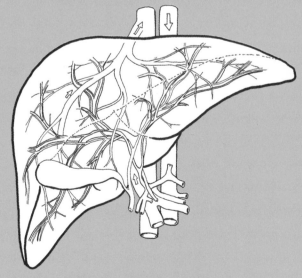

Smell 128
The significance of smells

The Tongue 130
How do we taste?

The Taste Buds 132
All over your tongue

Touch 134
How do we feel?

PART 5: BONES 136

What is Bone? 138
What keeps us standing?

Skeleton 140
The structure of the body

The Spine 142
The backbone

The Joints 144
How we bend and flex

The Muscles 146
How we move

How Do Muscles Work? 148
Pulling bones around

Tendons 150
Connecting muscles to bones

Hands and Feet 152
Gripping and Walking

Arms and Legs 154
Your limbs

The Kidneys 100
Cleaning the blood

Enzymes 102
Speeding up chemical reactions

The Gall Bladder 104
Storing bile

The Pancreas 106
Making hormones

The Bladder 108
Storing urine

The Tonsils 110
Helping prevent infection

PART 4: SENSES 112

The Eyes 114
How we see

Iris and Pupil 116
Eye colors

Color Vision 118
Seeing the spectrum of light

Tears 120
Why do we cry?

The Ears 122
How do we hear?

Quiet and Loud 124
Can sound harm you?

The Nose 126
How do we smell?

PART 6: REGULATION — 156

Cells — 158
The building blocks of the body

Types of Cell — 160
Millions of tiny specialists

Maintaining Cells — 162
Repair and replacement

The Metabolism — 164
Smooth running

The Lymph Nodes — 166
Your "alternative circulation"

The Immune System — 168
Fighting infection

Balance — 170
Staying upright

Body Temperature — 172
Staying warm

Perspiration — 174
Staying cool

Growing — 176
From birth to old age

Aging — 178
Why do we wear out?

Exercise — 180
Keeping the body fit

PART 7: ON THE OUTSIDE — 182

Hair — 184
Protecting the skin

Head Hair — 186
Straight, wavy, or curly?

Eyebrows and Eyelashes — 188
Protecting the eyes

Body Hair — 190
Our natural "blanket"

Nails — 192
Protecting the fingertips

Skin — 194
What holds us together?

Skin Color — 196
From black to white

Fingerprints — 198
Everyone's unique

PART 8: HEALTH — 200

Diseases and Medicine — 202
How we get sick

Bacteria and Viruses — 204
Our tiny enemies

Antibiotics — 206
Fighting infections

Surgery — 208
Operations and transplants

Coughs and Sneezes — 210
Mucus in the airways

Lung Health — 212
Breathing freely

Allergies — 214
From pollen to eggs

Broken Bones — 216
X-rays and casts

Wearing Glasses — 218
Seeing better

Microscopes — 220
Seeing the tiniest things

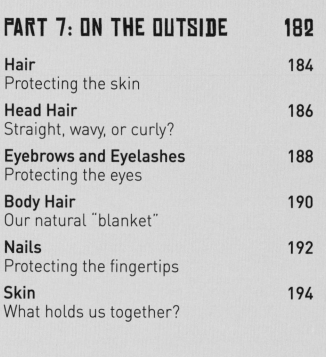

YOUR BODY

You are one of the most amazing systems on Earth. You contain billions of cells, thousands of miles of blood vessels, and a human brain—a thinking machine far more complex than any computer.

Turn over the page to see your whole body!

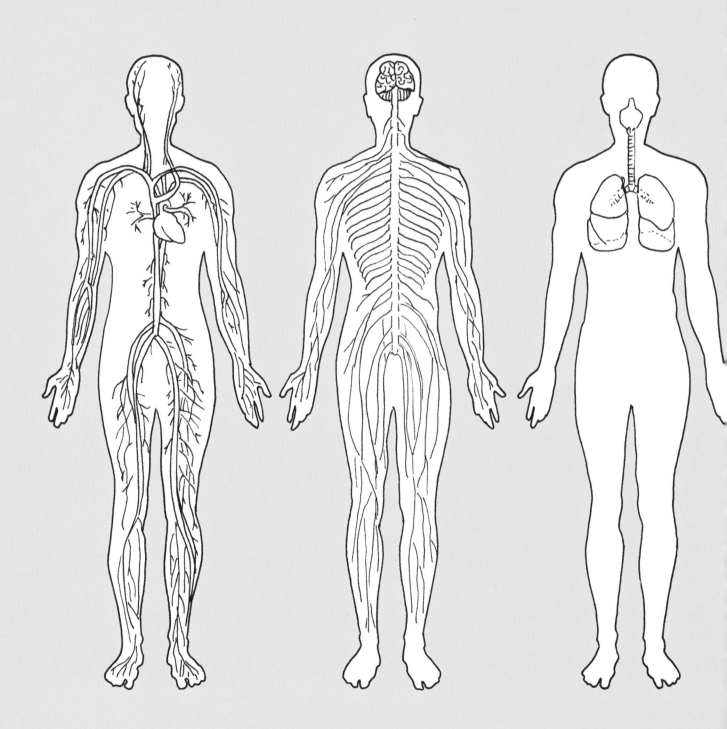

QUICK FACTS

The human body has more than 10 trillion **CELLS**.
Written in full, that's 10,000,000,000,000.

During an average lifetime (70 years) the heart **BEATS**
2.5 billion times.

Around 95 per cent of cells in the human body
are **BACTERIA**.

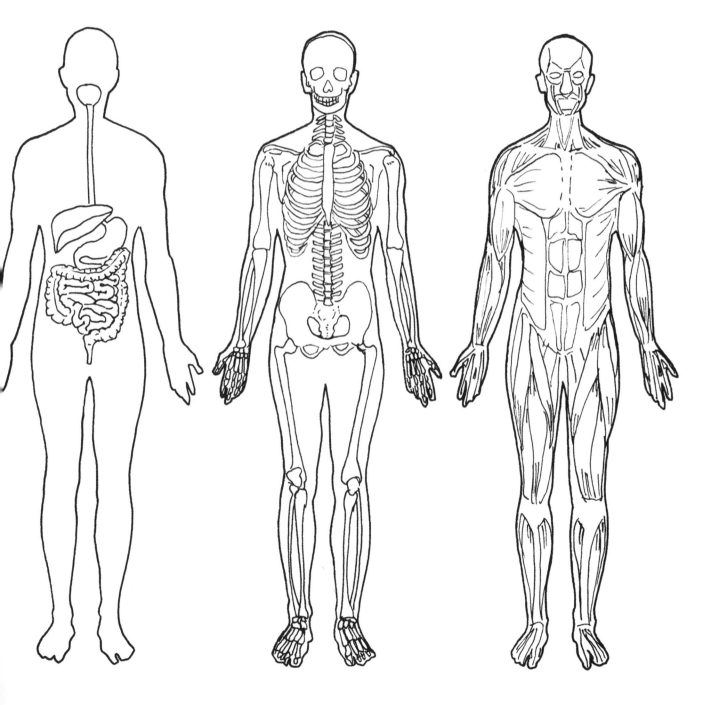

YOUR ORGANS

Every organ in the human body works as part of a team,
to keep you going and make you who you are.

You breathe air through
your **lungs**. These filter
oxygen into your blood.

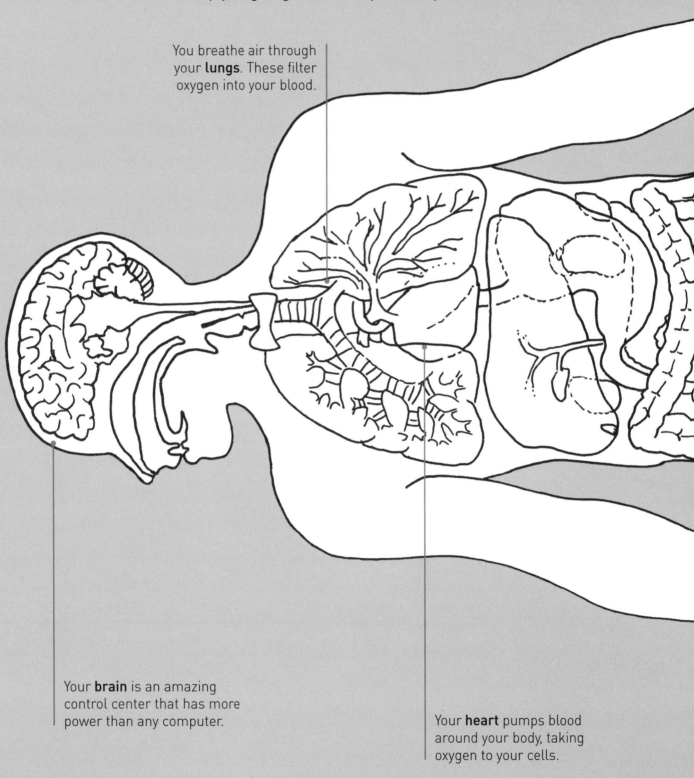

Your **brain** is an amazing
control center that has more
power than any computer.

Your **heart** pumps blood
around your body, taking
oxygen to your cells.

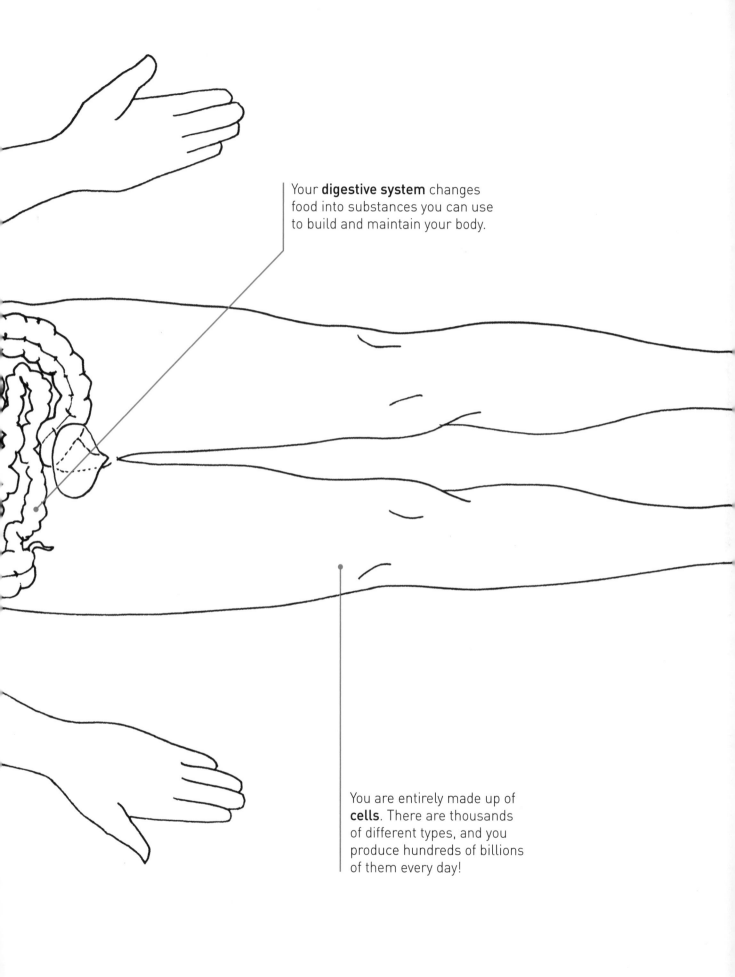

Your **digestive system** changes food into substances you can use to build and maintain your body.

You are entirely made up of **cells**. There are thousands of different types, and you produce hundreds of billions of them every day!

CONTROL CENTER

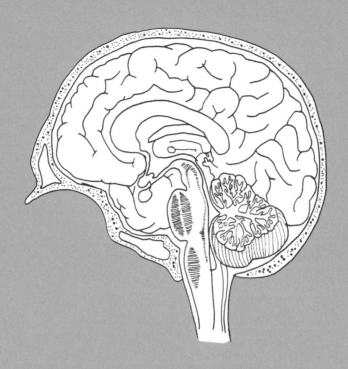

THE BRAIN

The brain is the body's control center. It coordinates all the messages that pass through the nervous system, giving us the ability to learn, reason, and feel. It also controls the body's automatic functions such as breathing, heartbeat, digestion, growth, and blood pressure.

QUICK FACTS

Our brains control our bodies by sending out billions of tiny electrical **SIGNALS** every second.

Even when asleep, the brain is just as **ACTIVE** as it is when awake, and sends nerve messages around itself.

The brain consumes about one-fifth of all the **ENERGY** used by the body.

Yet the brain forms only about **TWO PER CENT** of the whole body.

It uses 10 times as much energy for its **SIZE**, compared to other body parts.

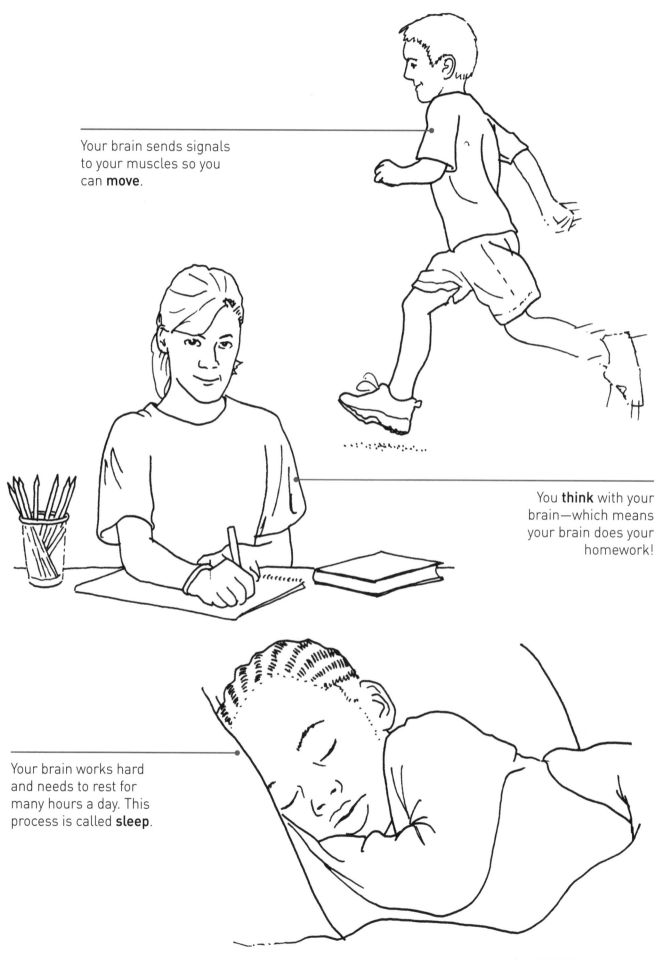

Your brain sends signals to your muscles so you can **move**.

You **think** with your brain—which means your brain does your homework!

Your brain works hard and needs to rest for many hours a day. This process is called **sleep**.

PARTS OF THE BRAIN

The brain is divided into three main regions, each with a different function.

The basic functioning of your body, thinking and movement, are all very different processes, and need to be controlled and monitored in different ways.

QUICK FACTS

The cerebrum makes up more than **FOUR-FIFTHS** of the whole brain, and accounts for 85 per cent of its weight.

The **WEIGHT** of an average adult brain is 3.09 lbs.

The **LARGEST** accurately measured normal human brain weighs 6.4 lbs.

The brain is protected by the **CRANIUM**, the domed part of your skull.

The cerebrum is more **DEVELOPED** in humans than in any animals.

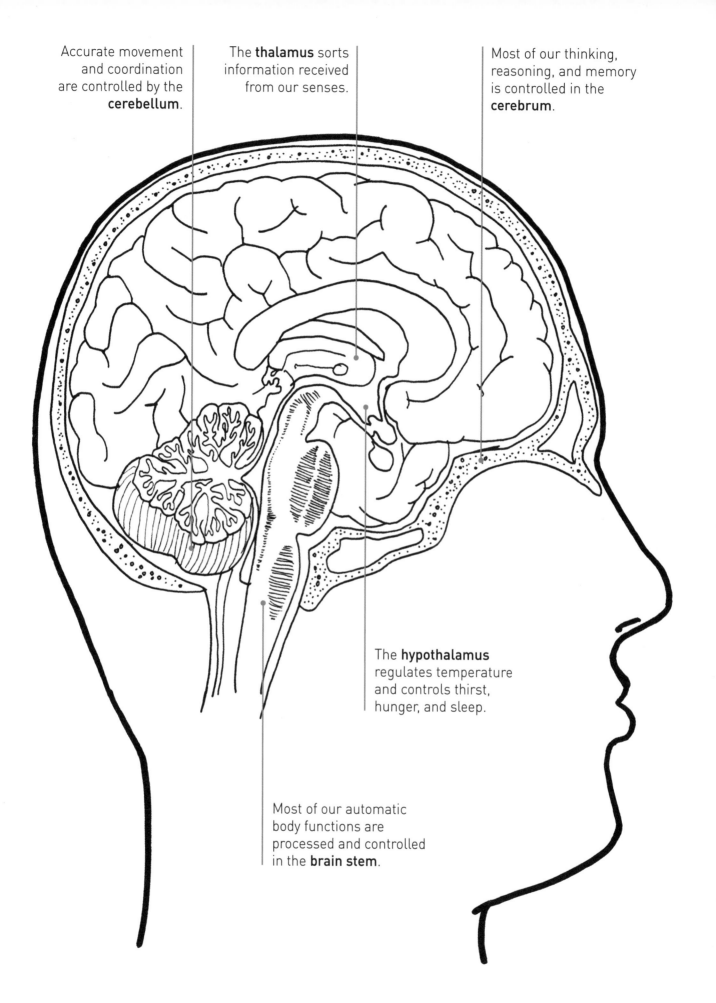

Accurate movement and coordination are controlled by the **cerebellum**.

The **thalamus** sorts information received from our senses.

Most of our thinking, reasoning, and memory is controlled in the **cerebrum**.

The **hypothalamus** regulates temperature and controls thirst, hunger, and sleep.

Most of our automatic body functions are processed and controlled in the **brain stem**.

LEFT AND RIGHT BRAIN

Each side of the brain controls the opposite side of the body. Usually the left side controls speaking, writing, and logical thought, while the right controls artistic abilities.

In a right-handed person, the left side of the brain is dominant. In a left-handed person, the right side is dominant.

QUICK FACTS

A person may **WRITE** with one hand, but use the other to carry out everyday tasks.

About four per cent of the population is **LEFT-HANDED**.

In the course of history many of the greatest **GENIUSES** have also been left-handed.

Leonardo da Vinci and Michelangelo, the greatest **SCULPTORS** of all times, were both left-handed.

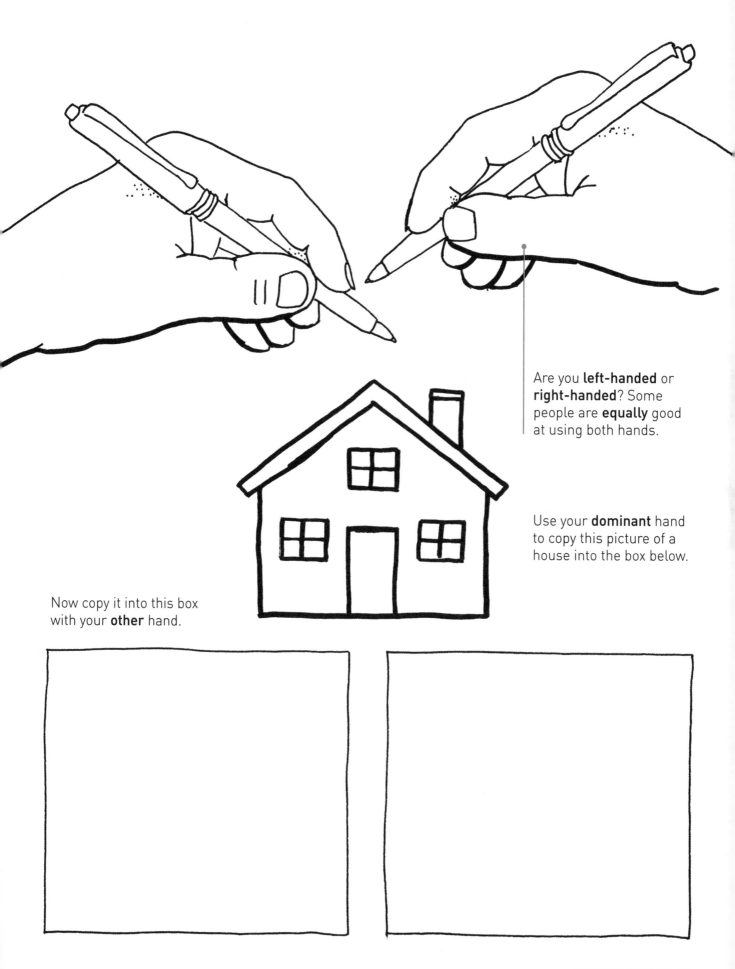

Are you **left-handed** or **right-handed**? Some people are **equally** good at using both hands.

Use your **dominant** hand to copy this picture of a house into the box below.

Now copy it into this box with your **other** hand.

MEMORY

Memory is the ability to store things that you experience and learn, ready for use in the future. Some things are remembered easily, such as dramatic events in our life. However, more ordinary things need to be rehearsed in the mind several times before they "stick".

QUICK FACTS

SENSORY MEMORY tells you what is happening around you, so you can move without bumping into things.

SHORT-TERM MEMORY allows you to remember a phone number and dial it, but only lasts for about 30 seconds.

LONG-TERM MEMORY stores things you have carefully memorized.

The sense of **SMELL** has powerful effects in retrieving memories. Often a smell, like the burning of a bonfire, can suddenly trigger a memory from many years ago.

The adult brain can memorize tens of thousands of **WORDS**.

How good is your **short-term memory**? Take a good look at the objects on this page, then turn the book face down and make a list of what you've seen. Then color in everything you remembered!

Apple

Flower

Cat

Bell

Cup

Cake

Glasses

Hand

Football

Truck

Board

Sandwich

Balloons

Present

Bird

Magnifying glass

Dog

Pencil

Seven

Tree

Flag

Trumpet

World

Bike

Book

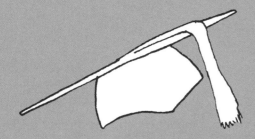

INTELLIGENCE

Sometimes we describe a very clever person as having "lots of brains". But we only have one brain each.

It is not the size of a brain that makes it clever, or the exact number of cells. It depends on how often its owner uses his or her brain, and in how much detail—by looking, listening, learning, remembering, using imagination, and having ideas.

QUICK FACTS

There is no link between the **SIZE** of a healthy brain and intelligence.

The brain contains more than 100 billion **NERVE CELLS**, about as many as there are stars in the Milky Way.

The brain also contains perhaps 10 times as many **"SUPPORT"** cells, called glia.

The average **FEMALE** brain is slightly smaller than the average male brain.

But the average female body is smaller, in comparison, to the average **MALE** body.

Compared to body size, women have slightly **LARGER** brains than men.

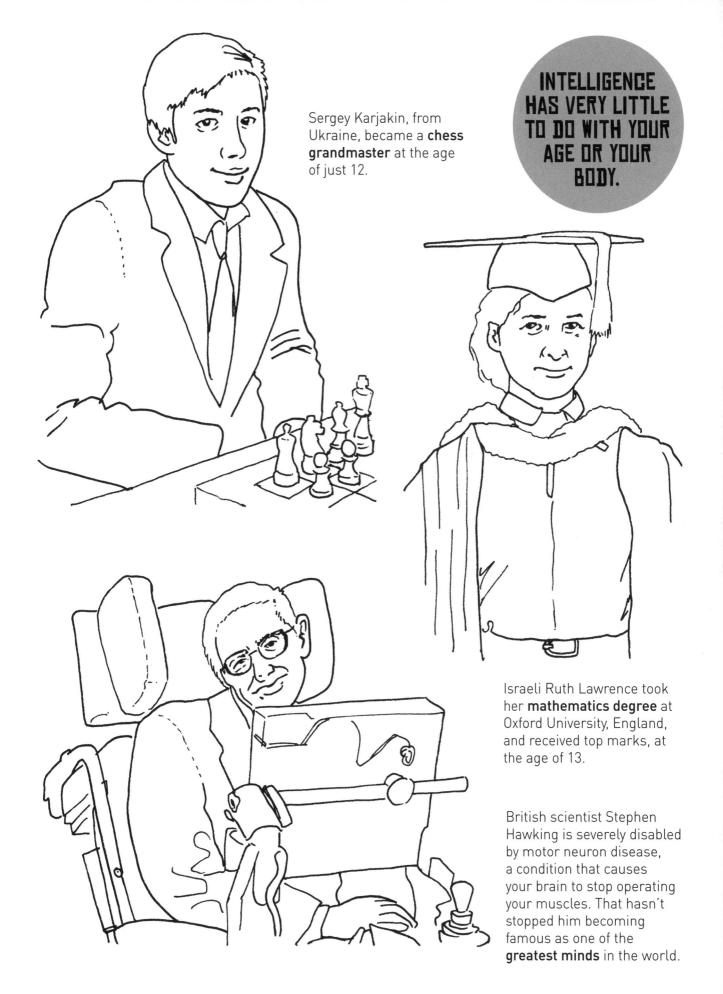

Sergey Karjakin, from Ukraine, became a **chess grandmaster** at the age of just 12.

Israeli Ruth Lawrence took her **mathematics degree** at Oxford University, England, and received top marks, at the age of 13.

British scientist Stephen Hawking is severely disabled by motor neuron disease, a condition that causes your brain to stop operating your muscles. That hasn't stopped him becoming famous as one of the **greatest minds** in the world.

THE GROWING BRAIN

The development of the brain happens quickly after conception. It continues to grow in size after birth, and makes new nerve connections throughout childhood.

QUICK FACTS

The brain does not make any new nerve cells after **BIRTH**.

But it does make new **CONNECTIONS** between nerve cells, perhaps millions every week, as we take in knowledge, develop skills, and learn new things.

From the age of about 20 years, the brain **SHRINKS** by about 1 gram of weight per year. This represents the loss of around 10,000 nerve cells each day.

Certain **DRUGS**, including alcohol, can speed this cell loss and make the brain shrink faster.

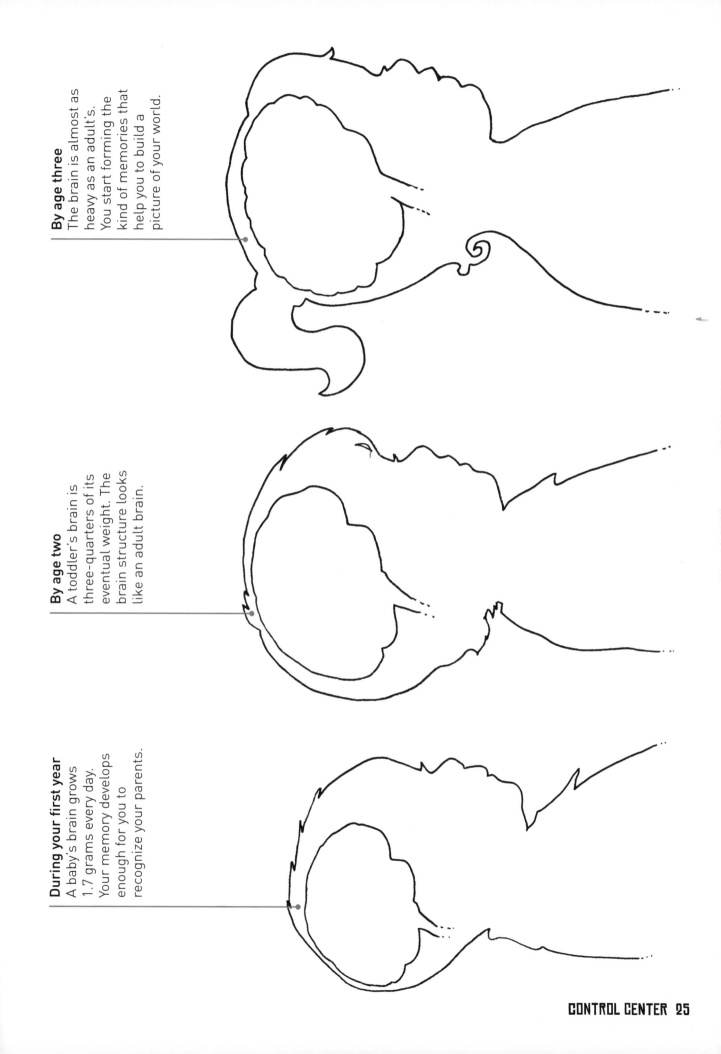

By age three
The brain is almost as heavy as an adult's. You start forming the kind of memories that help you to build a picture of your world.

By age two
A toddler's brain is three-quarters of its eventual weight. The brain structure looks like an adult brain.

During your first year
A baby's brain grows 1.7 grams every day. Your memory develops enough for you to recognize your parents.

NERVES

Messages are sent to the brain from different parts of the body and back through the nerves. A nerve impulse is like a very simple message: it's either on or off.

Because there are so many neurons (nerve paths) connected to one another, this simple signal is enough to carry the most complicated messages throughout the whole of the body's nervous system.

QUICK FACTS

A nerve **SIGNAL** is a tiny pulse of electricity, made by moving chemicals into and out of a nerve cell.

Nerves are bendy but **TOUGH**, so they can move easily at joints but withstand being squeezed by muscles.

There are nerves to **EVERY** body part, including the heart, lungs, and guts.

Individual nerve cells do not actually touch. The ends are separated by tiny gaps that are called **SYNAPSES**.

As a **nerve impulse** arrives at the junction between two nerve cells, it is carried across the gap or synapse by chemicals called neurotransmitters. These contact sensitive areas in the next nerve cell, and the nerve impulse is carried along.

Neurotransmitter

Nerve gap (synapse)

Nerve membrane

Vesicle (stores drops of neurotransmitter)

Arriving nerve impulse

SYNAPSES ARE SO SMALL THAT SCIENTISTS HAVE TO USE SPECIAL ELECTRON MICROSCOPES TO STUDY THEM.

THE NERVOUS SYSTEM

We all have a nerve system to control our every movement and action, and every process that happens inside the body.

Your nervous system is made up of your brain, spinal cord, and nerves. It works by sending tiny electrical signals called nerve impulses. Millions of these travel around the body and brain every second, like the busiest computer network.

QUICK FACTS

Nerve **IMPULSES** travel along the largest nerve fibers at 295 ft per second!

When you hurt a finger you probably feel the touch first, and then the pain starts a moment later. This is because the signals for touch travel **FASTER** along the nerves than the signals for pain.

All the nerves in the body, taken out and joined end to end, would stretch about **62 MILES**.

The longest single nerve **FIBERS**, in the legs, are up to a yard in length.

The **THICKEST** nerve in the human body is the sciatic nerve, located in the hip and thigh. It is about the width of its owner's thumb.

The **SPINAL CORD** is usually the width of its owner's little finger.

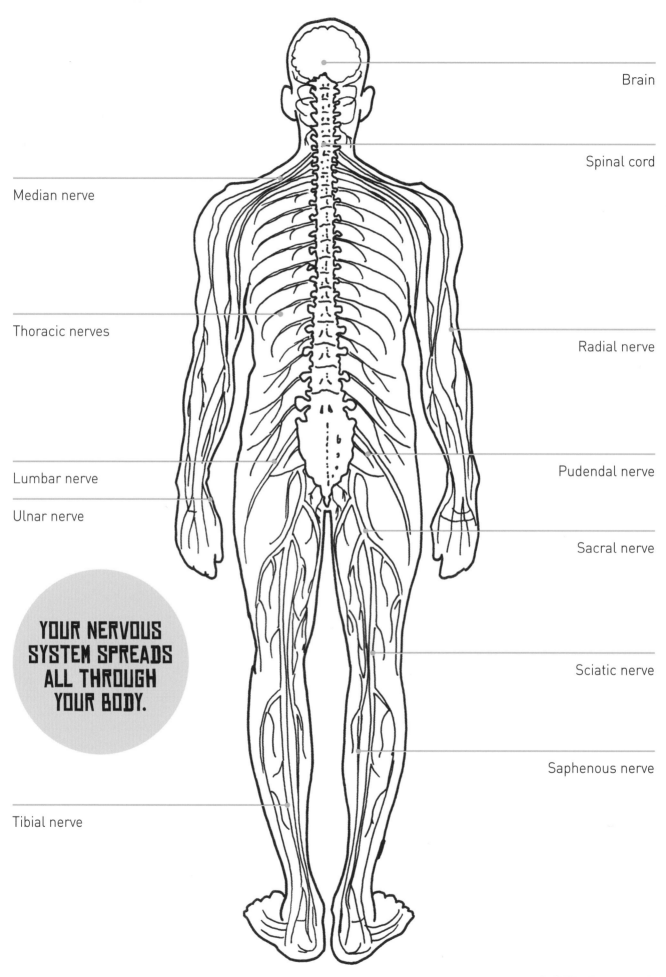

Brain

Spinal cord

Median nerve

Thoracic nerves

Radial nerve

Lumbar nerve

Pudendal nerve

Ulnar nerve

Sacral nerve

YOUR NERVOUS SYSTEM SPREADS ALL THROUGH YOUR BODY.

Sciatic nerve

Saphenous nerve

Tibial nerve

SLEEP

Thinking, seeing, and all other mental activities use up a lot of energy. So the brain and other nerve centers need a rest.

Sleep clears away our tiredness, and when we wake up we feel rested. Even while the body sleeps, its nerve systems are active, continuously monitoring and adjusting the internal processes, and checking the outside world for danger.

QUICK FACTS

Your **HEART** never stops, but it beats slower while at rest.

During a night's sleep, a person may change position as many as **40** times.

Every 24 hours the average **NEWBORN** baby needs 20 hours of sleep, a 10-year-old 10 hours, and an adult 7–8 hours.

Older people tend to sleep more hours overall but often in several sessions, such as **NAPS** during the day.

What actually **WAKES US UP** is something that scientists find hard to explain.

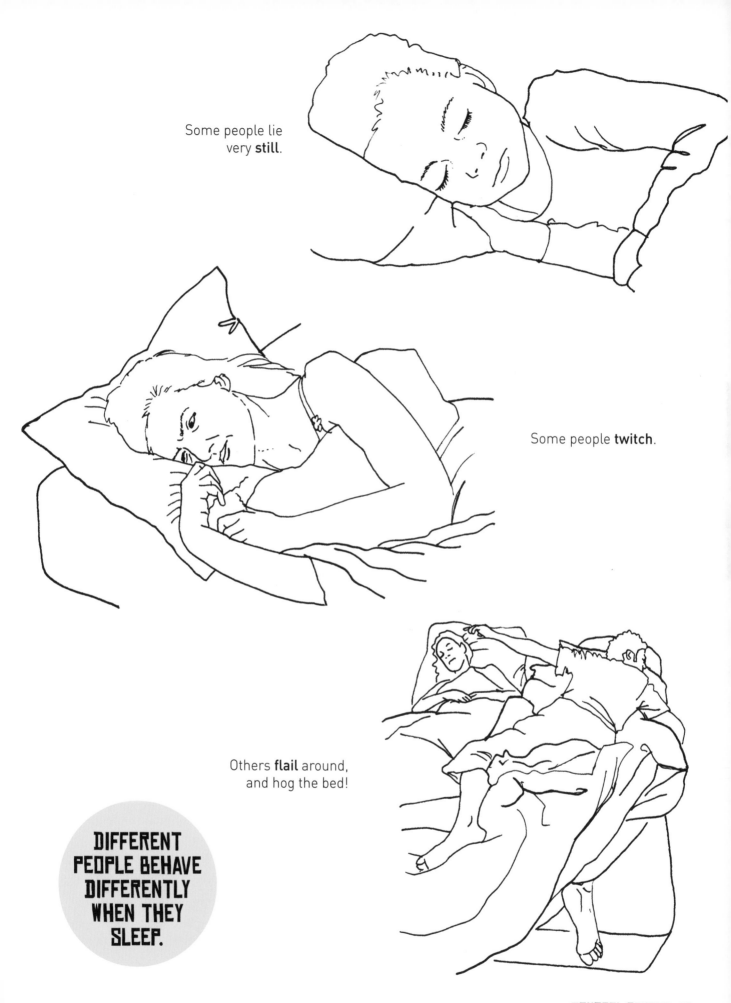

Some people lie very **still**.

Some people **twitch**.

Others **flail** around, and hog the bed!

DIFFERENT PEOPLE BEHAVE DIFFERENTLY WHEN THEY SLEEP.

DREAMS

All our dreams have something to do with our emotions, fears, longings, wishes, needs, and memories.

But something on the "outside" may influence what we dream. If you are hungry, tired, or cold, your dreams may well include these feelings. If the covers have slipped off your bed, you may dream you are on an iceberg.

QUICK FACTS

During a night's sleep, you may have as many as **FIVE** dreams.

There are people called psychoanalysts who have made a special study of **WHY** people dream. They believe dreams are expressions of wishes that didn't come true.

According to this theory, our **INHIBITIONS** are also asleep while we dream.

DAYDREAMING is a form of dreaming done while we are awake. That's the only difference, since we are so relaxed that we pay no attention to the world around us.

HEART
AND
LUNGS

WHAT IS BLOOD?

Blood carries useful substances such as oxygen and nutrients to all the body parts. Pumped by the heart, it flows through tubes called blood vessels.

It also collects waste and unwanted substances, and these are removed mainly by the kidneys. However, apart from this delivery and collection service, blood does much, much more.

QUICK FACTS

Blood is **WARM** and works like the liquid in a central heating system. It absorbs warmth from the busy parts such as the heart and muscles, and spreads it out to cooler parts like the skin.

Just over half of blood is **PLASMA**, a pale yellow, sweet-smelling, sticky fluid.

Over nine-tenths of blood is **WATER**.

Blood contains disease-fighting **ANTIBODIES**. It helps seal cuts and wounds, by clotting.

Your blood makes up about eight per cent of your body **WEIGHT**.

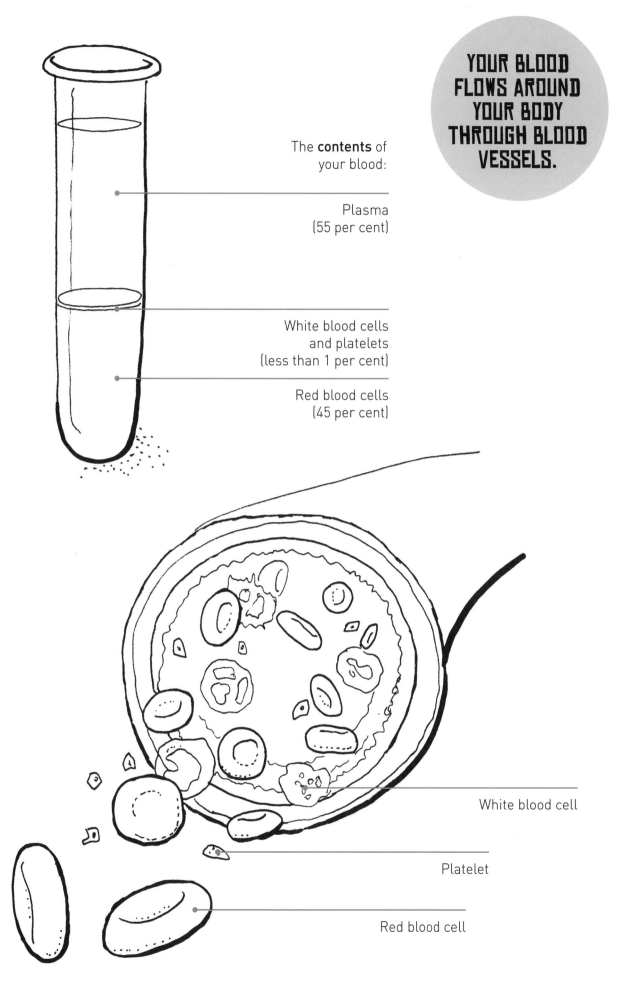

The **contents** of your blood:

Plasma
(55 per cent)

White blood cells
and platelets
(less than 1 per cent)

Red blood cells
(45 per cent)

White blood cell

Platelet

Red blood cell

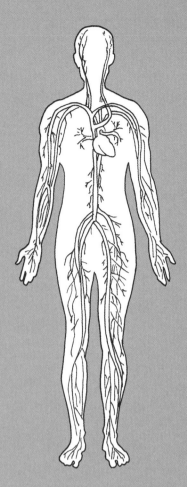

THE HEART

In the center of your chest, below a thin layer of skin, muscle, and bone, sits your heart. This simple, yet essential, pump carries blood to and from your body's billions of cells, non-stop, day and night.

The heart is between the lungs. It tips slightly to the left side, which is why people think it is on the left side of the body.

QUICK FACTS

Without the heart's second-by-second **COLLECTION** and **DELIVERY** service, your cells—and your body—would die.

The heart is about the size of its owner's clenched **FIST**. As you grow from a child into an adult, your heart grows at the same rate as your fist.

The heart contains the **AORTA**, the largest artery in the body. It is about the diameter of a garden hose.

An adult has an average resting **HEART RATE** of about 75 beats per minute.

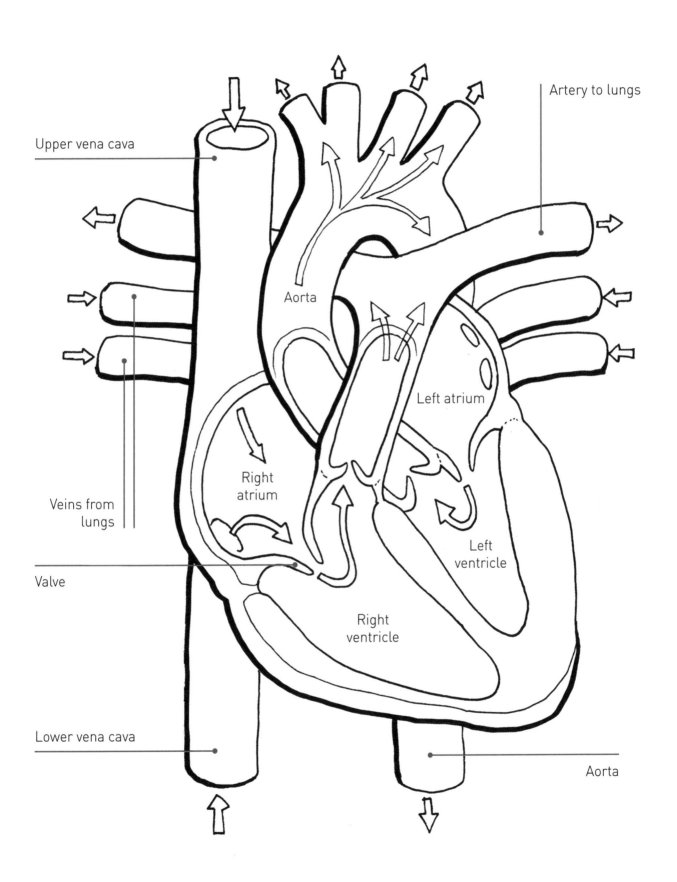

Upper vena cava

Artery to lungs

Aorta

Left atrium

Veins from
lungs

Right
atrium

Left
ventricle

Valve

Right
ventricle

Lower vena cava

Aorta

RED BLOOD CELLS

Red blood cells carry oxygen around your system. They are among the most numerous cells in the body, with 25,000 billion in an average person. They are also among the smallest cells.

QUICK FACTS

Each red cell is shaped like a **DONUT**, without the hole completely poked through.

Each red blood cell **LIVES** for three or four months, then dies and is broken apart.

About three million red blood cells **DIE** every second— and the same number of new ones are made.

A red blood cell can make a full **CIRCUIT** of the human body in just 30 seconds.

Your blood is made up almost entirely of **bright red** cells—except for a few white cells and platelets. Can you spot the odd ones out, and leave them white as you color the rest?

WHITE BLOOD CELLS

As well as the red cells, our blood also carries white blood cells, which help to fight off disease.

All of the cells and nutrients are carried in a pale yellow, thick liquid which is called plasma. The other materials carried in the plasma include a substance called fibrinogen, which helps the blood to clot when we cut ourselves.

QUICK FACTS

White blood cells eat **WASTE** such as pieces of old, broken-down cells.

Blood is mostly made up of plasma and red blood cells. White blood cells form less than **ONE PER CENT** of blood.

A white blood cell is not really white, but almost **TRANSPARENT**.

White blood cells, like red blood cells and platelets, are made in the jelly-like **MARROW** inside bones.

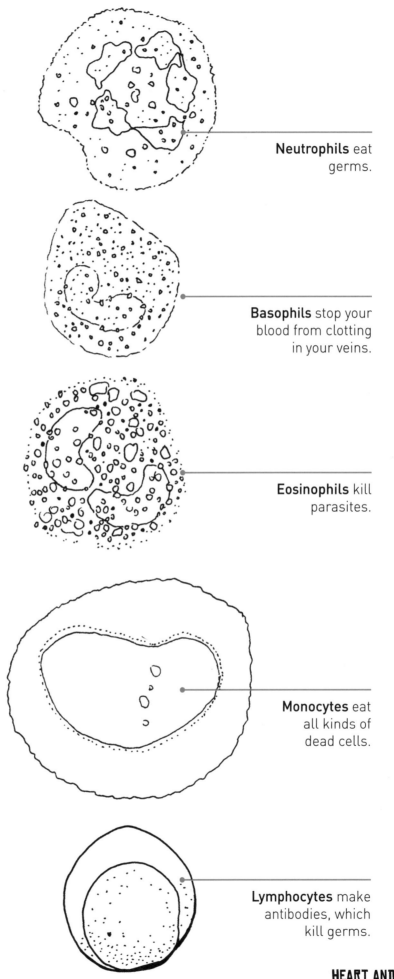

Neutrophils eat germs.

Basophils stop your blood from clotting in your veins.

Eosinophils kill parasites.

Monocytes eat all kinds of dead cells.

Lymphocytes make antibodies, which kill germs.

VEINS AND ARTERIES

Blood is pumped around your body in a continuous flow from the heart. It travels inside a network of tubes called blood vessels—arteries, veins, and capillaries.

The blood in arteries comes straight from the heart and is pumped under pressure, so the artery walls are thick and muscular. Veins return blood to the heart, and because the pressure is lower, they have thinner walls than arteries.

QUICK FACTS

Veins look **BLUE** because of a trick of the light. In reality, this blood is a very dark red.

The blood in your veins travels quite slowly, and many large veins have **VALVES** to stop the blood from draining backward toward your legs and feet.

In general, arteries lie **DEEP** within the body, and veins nearer the **SURFACE**.

"Going for the **JUGULAR**" means attacking someone at their weakest point. It refers to the vulnerability of the jugular vein, which is in your neck.

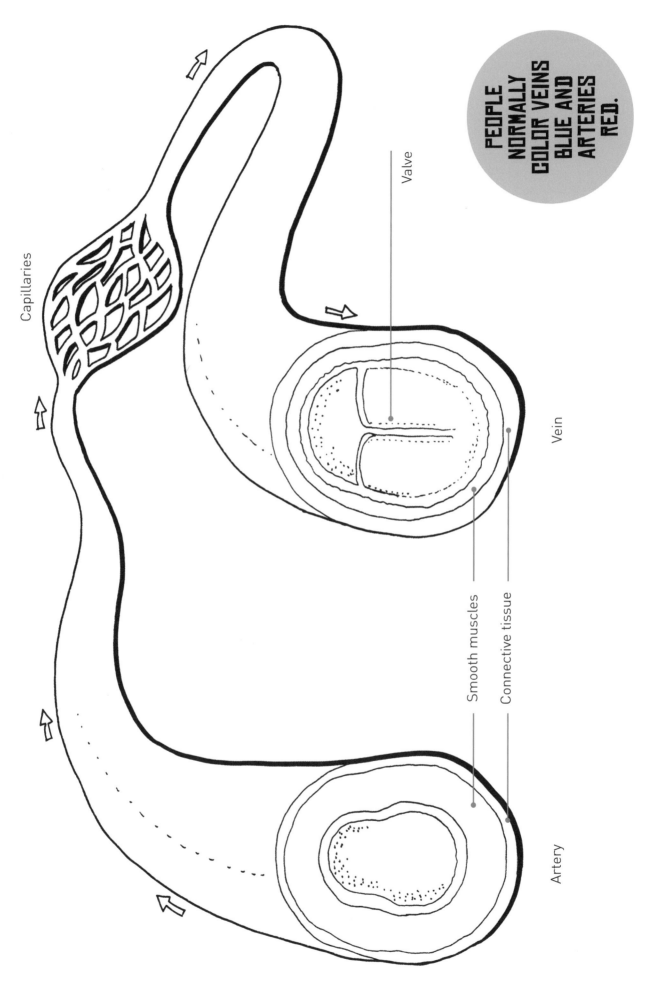

Capillaries

Valve

Vein

Smooth muscles

Connective tissue

Artery

CAPILLARIES

Blood moves from arteries to veins through tiny capillaries. The capillaries also allow excess fluid to escape from the blood.

They are too small to be seen without a microscope, and so narrow that red blood cells have to squash themselves up to pass through.

QUICK FACTS

The cells in blood flow through a capillary for only **HALF A SECOND** before they move on into small veins.

Laid out end to end, an adult's veins, arteries, and capillaries would be about **60,000 MILES** long!

About one-sixth of all the body's **BLOOD** is in the arteries, almost three-quarters is in the veins, and less than one-twentieth is in the tiny capillaries inside the organs.

If all your capillaries were ironed flat, they would cover a **SOCCER PITCH**.

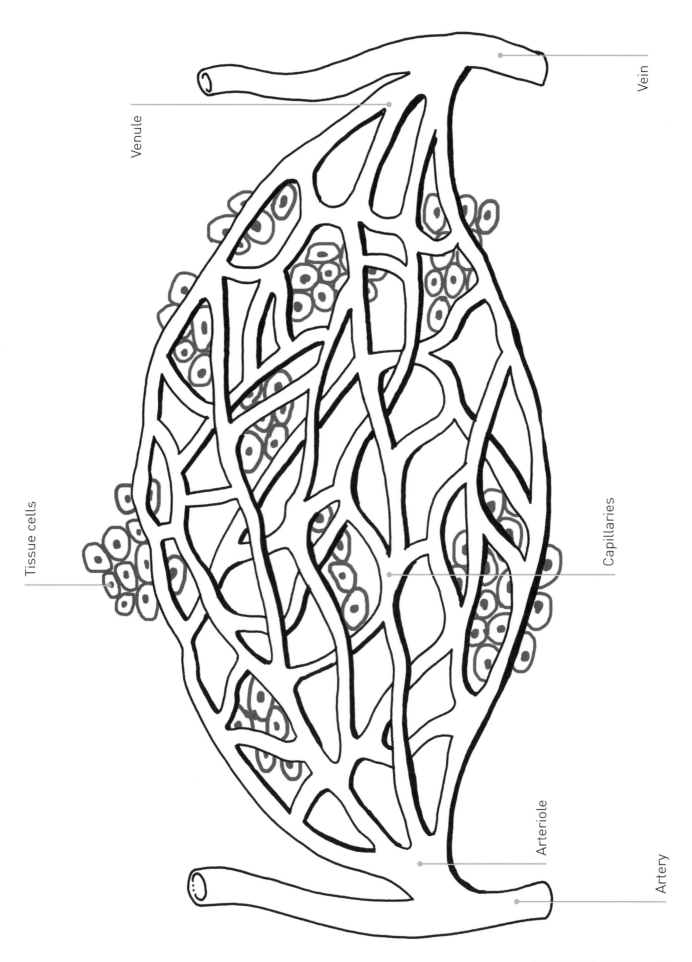

Venule

Vein

Tissue cells

Capillaries

Arteriole

Artery

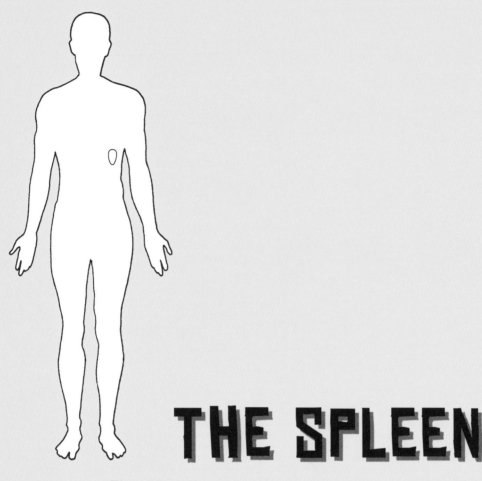

THE SPLEEN

The spleen is one of the main filters of the blood. It removes old, worn-out, and abnormal blood cells. This applies in particular to red blood cells, but white cells and platelets are also filtered selectively by the spleen when it is necessary.

QUICK FACTS

The spleen is the largest collection of **LYMPH** tissue in the body.

It is about the size of a clenched **FIST**.

It **WEIGHS** just over five ounces but can be half or twice this, according to blood content and the body's state of health.

The spleen is situated in the top left-hand corner of the abdomen, just below the diaphragm. Because of its relatively exposed position, it is frequently **DAMAGED** in accidents and has to be removed.

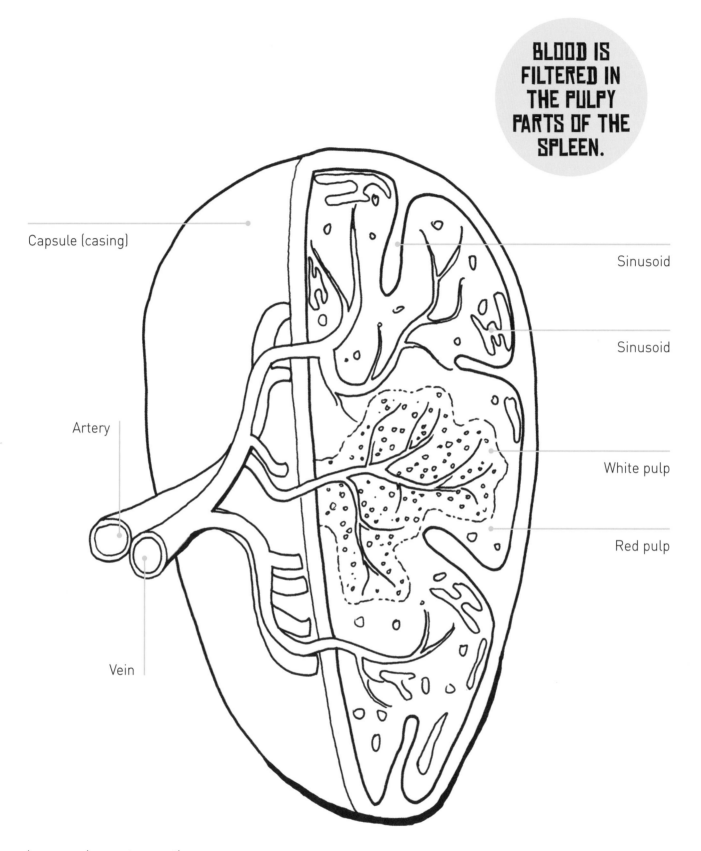

Capsule (casing)

Sinusoid

Sinusoid

Artery

White pulp

Red pulp

Vein

In some circumstances the spleen has a major role in the **manufacture** of new red blood cells. This does not happen in normal adults, but in people who have a bone marrow disease.

BLOOD GROUPS

It is important to know what blood group someone is if they are about to donate blood. This is because certain kinds, or groups, of blood, may form clots when mixed together. This could cause the recipient of the blood to die.

QUICK FACTS

The process of putting blood from one person into another is called a **TRANSFUSION**.

The **FOUR** different human blood groups were discovered in 1900. Before this, blood transfusions often failed.

ABO is the system for testing blood for its group. You can be in blood group A, B, AB, or O.

Our individual blood group is determined by our parents', and set at the time of our **CONCEPTION**.

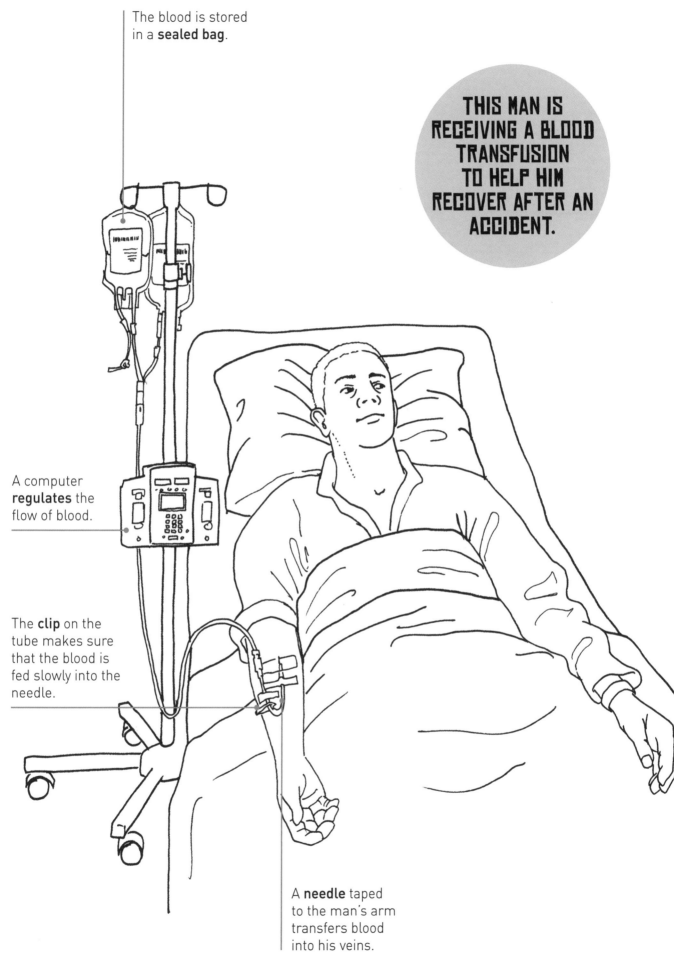

The blood is stored in a **sealed bag**.

THIS MAN IS RECEIVING A BLOOD TRANSFUSION TO HELP HIM RECOVER AFTER AN ACCIDENT.

A computer **regulates** the flow of blood.

The **clip** on the tube makes sure that the blood is fed slowly into the needle.

A **needle** taped to the man's arm transfers blood into his veins.

BLOOD CLOTTING

When you cut yourself, the blood clots to prevent the wound from bleeding.

Clotting is caused by substances in the blood. Together with small particles called platelets, these substances produce masses of fine mesh called fibrin when they are exposed to air.

QUICK FACTS

SCABS are made of clotted blood. They protect new skin while it grows.

For a small **CUT**, this process usually takes a few days.

HAEMOPHILIA is an inherited deficiency in which the substance necessary for blood clotting is missing. Even a slight cut or bump can be dangerous if the bleeding cannot be stopped.

Queen Victoria carried the **GENE** for haemophilia. Of her nine children, two of her daughters inherited the gene, and one of her sons suffered from the condition.

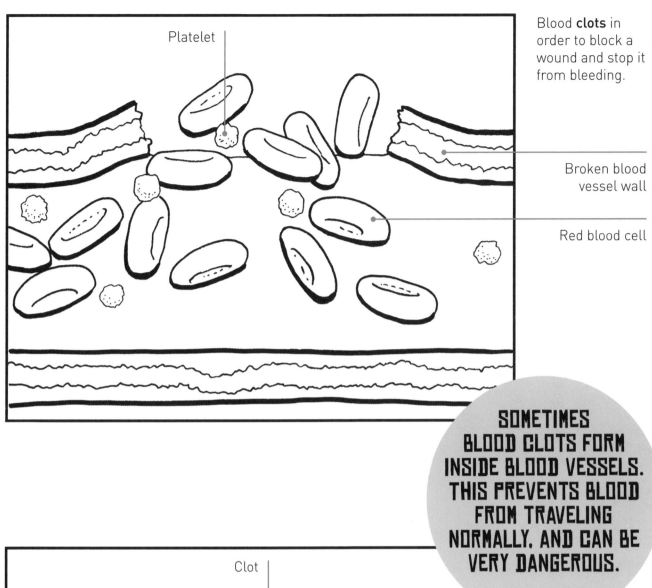

Platelet

Blood **clots** in order to block a wound and stop it from bleeding.

Broken blood vessel wall

Red blood cell

SOMETIMES BLOOD CLOTS FORM INSIDE BLOOD VESSELS. THIS PREVENTS BLOOD FROM TRAVELING NORMALLY, AND CAN BE VERY DANGEROUS.

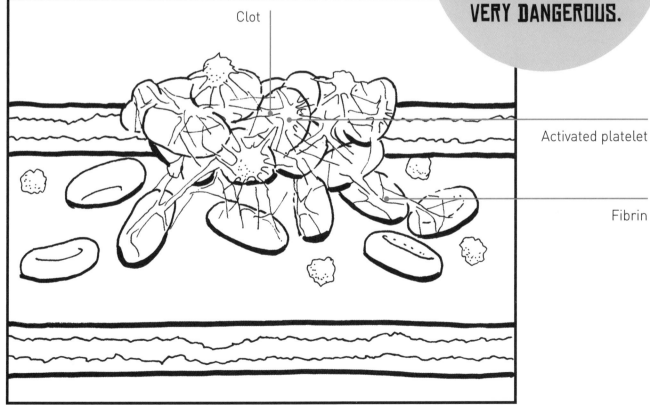

Clot

Activated platelet

Fibrin

WHY DO WE BREATHE?

Breathing is when you draw air in through your nose and mouth, and into your lungs. Like all your movements, it relies on muscle power.

We breathe in order to get oxygen from the air. Oxygen is the gas our bodies use to convert nutrients into energy. We breathe out to get rid of carbon dioxide, a waste gas that our bodies cannot use.

QUICK FACTS

INHALED air contains 20 per cent oxygen, 0.03 per cent carbon dioxide, and the rest is nitrogen.

EXHALED air contains 16 per cent oxygen, and the carbon dioxide is increased by more than a hundred times to four per cent.

The average person at **REST** breathes in and out about 10–14 times per minute.

If you sing or play an **INSTRUMENT** like a trumpet, you need lots of puff. Learn to use the muscle under your lungs to get more lung power.

We breathe **heavily** after exercise, in order to take in more oxygen.

WE BREATHE IN DIFFERENT WAYS AT DIFFERENT TIMES.

We breathe **smoothly** and **deeply** when we are concentrating, for example while doing homework.

Sometimes breathing while asleep makes you **snore**! There are several different causes for snoring.

HOW DO WE BREATHE?

When we breathe, air enters through the nose or mouth and travels down the windpipe. The windpipe forks into other tubes called bronchi, which lead into the lungs.

Breathe in deeply and watch your ribs rise and your chest expand. Your muscles make your chest bigger and stretch the spongy lungs inside.

QUICK FACTS

You breathe every few **SECONDS** throughout your life, even when you are asleep.

The right lung is often a little **LARGER** than the left.

Underwater animals, like fish, have breathing organs called **GILLS** instead of lungs. These can take in oxygen from the water.

To enable us to breathe underwater, humans need an **OXYGEN TANK**, because if our lungs filled with water we would drown.

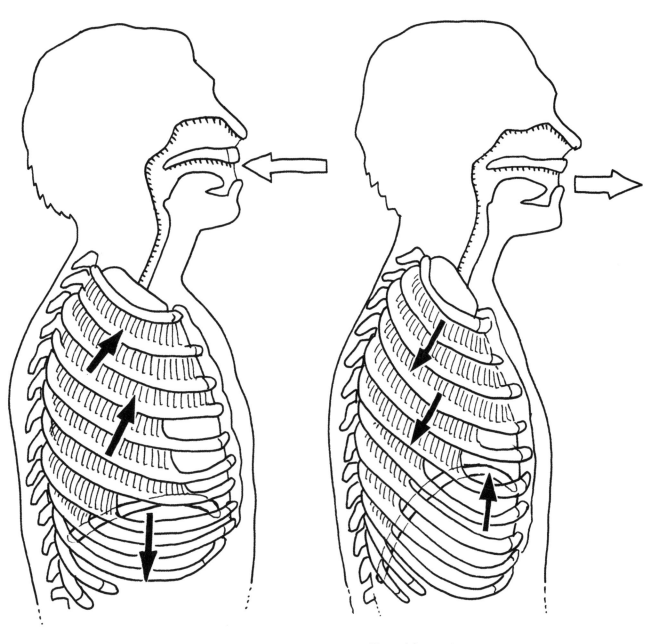

Breathing in
Your ribcage is **pushed out**

Your diaphragm is **pushed down**

Your lungs **expand**

Air **enters** the oral cavity (mouth)

Breathing out
Your ribcage is **pulled in**

Your diaphragm **rises**

Your lungs **contract**

Air **exits** the oral cavity (mouth)

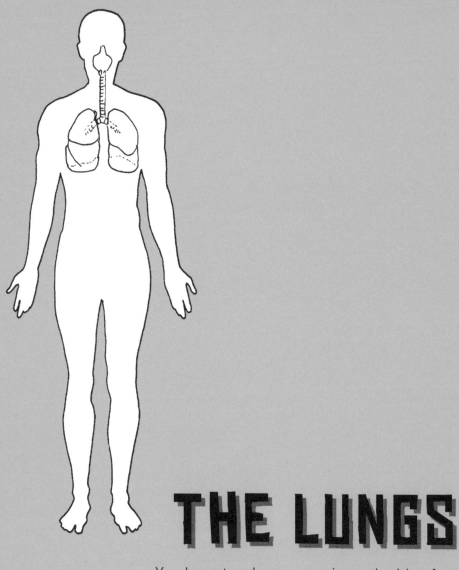

THE LUNGS

You have two lungs, one in each side of your chest, enclosed by an airtight box.

When you breathe in and out, your lungs go up and down rather like balloons, but they aren't just hollow bags. They are spongy organs made up of tightly packed tissue, nerves, and blood vessels.

QUICK FACTS

The whole breathing apparatus is designed to bring fresh **AIR** as close as possible to the blood.

The left lung has two main parts, or **LOBES**, and a scooped-out shape where the heart fits.

The right lung has three lobes and is on average about one-fifth **BIGGER** than the left lung.

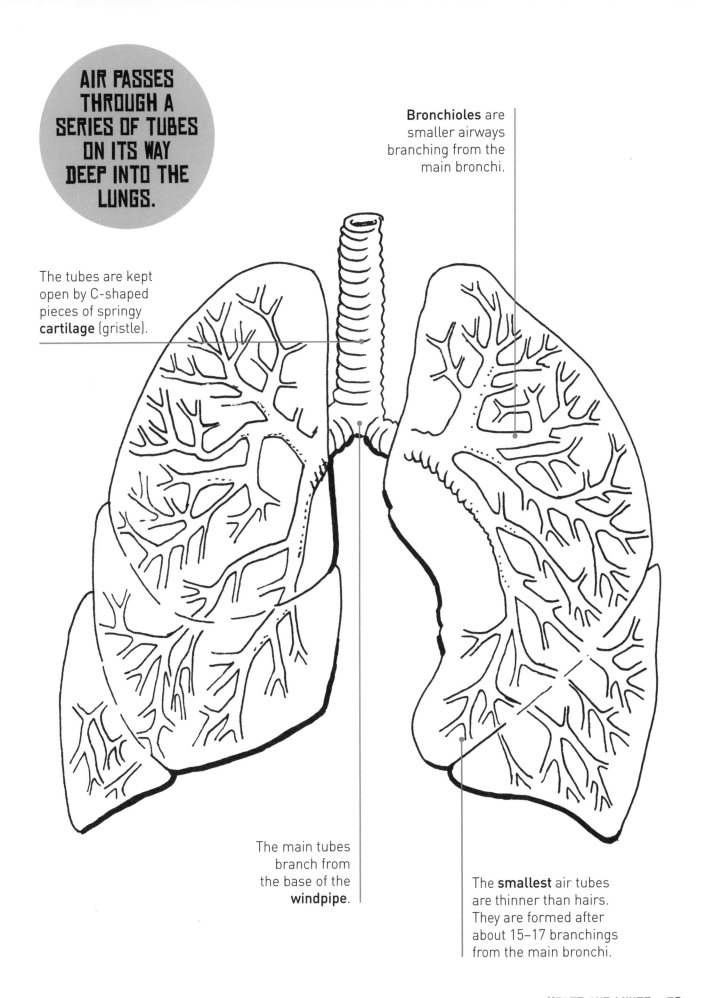

AIR PASSES THROUGH A SERIES OF TUBES ON ITS WAY DEEP INTO THE LUNGS.

Bronchioles are smaller airways branching from the main bronchi.

The tubes are kept open by C-shaped pieces of springy **cartilage** (gristle).

The main tubes branch from the base of the **windpipe**.

The **smallest** air tubes are thinner than hairs. They are formed after about 15–17 branchings from the main bronchi.

INSIDE THE LUNGS

The places where oxygen is taken into the body are tiny bubble-shaped spaces deep in the lungs called alveoli. Alveoli are bunched at the end of the smallest airways, the bronchioles.

The walls of the alveoli are so thin that oxygen and carbon dioxide can pass through them.

QUICK FACTS

There are 250–300 million alveoli in each **LUNG**.

If the **WALLS** of the alveoli could be spread out flat, they would cover about half a tennis court!

Alveoli are delicate, and can be damaged by many different things, thus causing us to **COUGH**.

Each alveolar **DUCT** in the lungs supplies about 20 alveoli.

The very thin walls of each alveolus contain networks of extremely small blood vessels called **CAPILLARIES**.

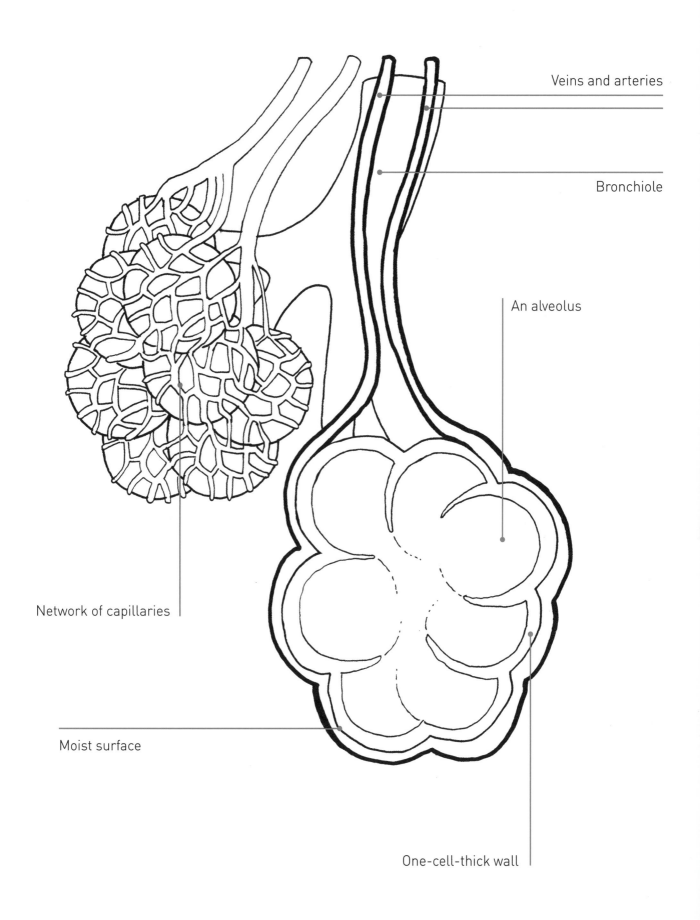

Veins and arteries

Bronchiole

An alveolus

Network of capillaries

Moist surface

One-cell-thick wall

SPEECH

Air passing out of the lungs has a useful extra effect: speech.

At the top of the windpipe, in the sides of the voice box, are two stiff, shelf-like folds called the vocal cords. Criss-crossed muscles in the voice box can pull the cords together so that air passes through a narrow slit between them and makes them vibrate, creating sounds.

QUICK FACTS

You use the muscles of your throat, mouth, and lips to form the sounds into **WORDS**.

When we actually learn to talk, our speech depends on the the development of the **BRAIN**.

There are nine pieces of **CARTILAGE** (gristle) in the voice box.

The voice box shows on the outside of the throat as a lump called the **ADAM'S APPLE**. This is larger in men than in women.

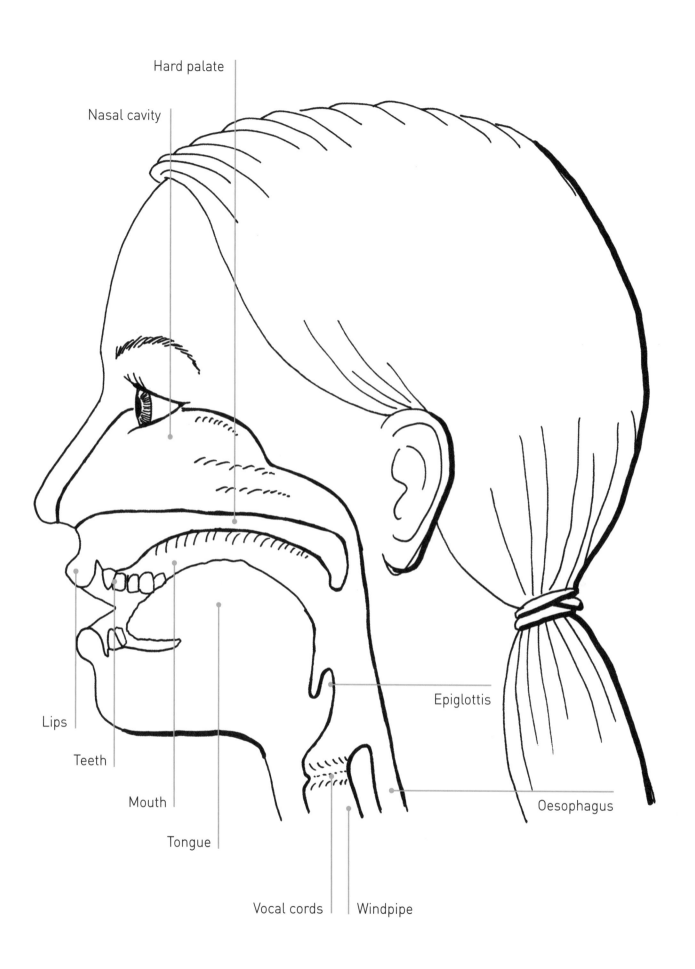

Hard palate

Nasal cavity

Lips

Teeth

Mouth

Tongue

Vocal cords

Windpipe

Epiglottis

Oesophagus

DIFFERENT VOICES

The pitch of your voice is determined by the size of your voice box. Women's voices are usually pitched higher than men's because their vocal cords are about 0.2 in. shorter. Children's are even shorter.

The muscles of the voice box can alter the shape of the cords to produce different sounds.

QUICK FACTS

About 19 muscles in the voice box alter the **LENGTH** of the vocal cords to make the sounds of speech.

The harder the air is forced out, the **LOUDER** the sounds.

The more **RELAXED** your vocal cords are, the **LOWER** the sounds.

At the age of puberty a boy's voice "**BREAKS**". The voice box enlarges, due to the effect of the male hormone, testosterone, and the vocal cords become longer.

Few women have **visible** Adam's apples.

Some men's are very **prominent**!

WHAT DOES YOUR DAD'S OR BROTHER'S LOOK LIKE?

SPEECH WITHOUT SPEAKING

Although many people think of speech as our main way of communicating, we don't have to use spoken words. Body language is the series of gestures and movements we make with our face, head, arms, hands, and indeed our whole body, to signal thoughts and feelings.

Head and facial gestures can say a lot about how we feel.

QUICK FACTS

People who are **TIRED** tend to hunch up and look smaller.

People who are excited and **HAPPY** make big, confident gestures.

CONFIDENT people tend to show they are sure of themselves by standing up straight.

People's gestures often mean **DIFFERENT** things in different countries.

However, there are six facial expressions that are the **SAME** around the world: happiness, sadness, anger, disgust, fear, and surprise.

People who can't speak learn a language called **signing**, in which hands and fingers are used. Here are some of the gestures used in American Sign Language (ASL).

BOY

GIRL

YES

NO

MAN

WOMAN

HELLO

GOODBYE

PLEASE

SORRY

THANK YOU

FOOD

HUNGRY

BATHROOM

EATING AND DIGESTION

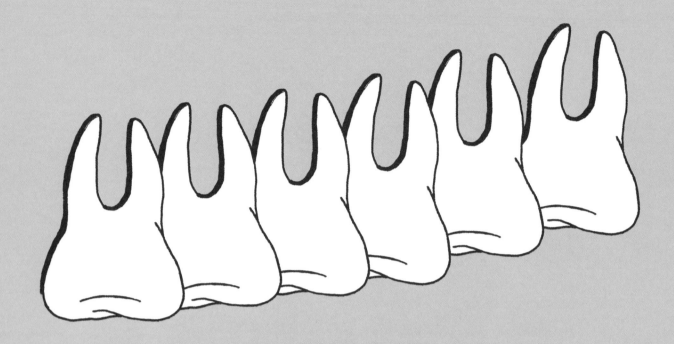

TEETH

Humans have four kinds of teeth: incisors, canines, premolars, and molars. They are differently shaped, so they can carry out different jobs.

QUICK FACTS

Your back teeth are **BUMPY** on top. They work together, grinding food between the bumps.

No two sets of teeth are the same. Your teeth are as **UNIQUE** as your fingerprints.

As the **SURFACE** of a tooth wears away, the tooth grows farther out of its socket, exposing the root.

WISDOM teeth are a mystery. Nobody has discovered exactly why we have them, and what their purpose is!

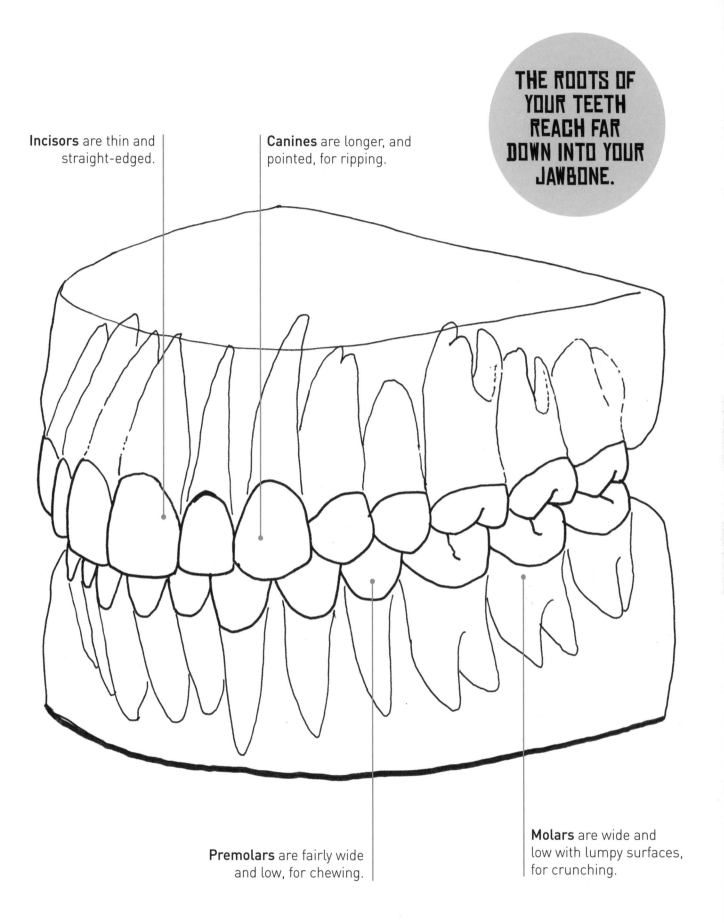

Incisors are thin and straight-edged.

Canines are longer, and pointed, for ripping.

Premolars are fairly wide and low, for chewing.

Molars are wide and low with lumpy surfaces, for crunching.

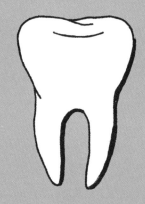

INSIDE A TOOTH

Each tooth has two main parts. The root anchors it firmly in the gum, to withstand the tremendous pressures that are exerted when you bite and chew hard foods like nuts. The crown is the visible part above the gum. It is covered with whitish enamel, which is the hardest substance in the entire body.

QUICK FACTS

PULP is the innermost layer of a tooth. It consists of connective tissue, blood vessels, and nerves.

DENTINE is harder than bone, and takes up most of a tooth. It consists mainly of mineral salts and water, but also has some living cells.

ENAMEL is the hardest tissue in the body. It enables a tooth to withstand the pressure placed on it during chewing.

CEMENTUM overlays the dentine in the root of the tooth. In most cases, the cementum and enamel meet where the root ends and the crown begins.

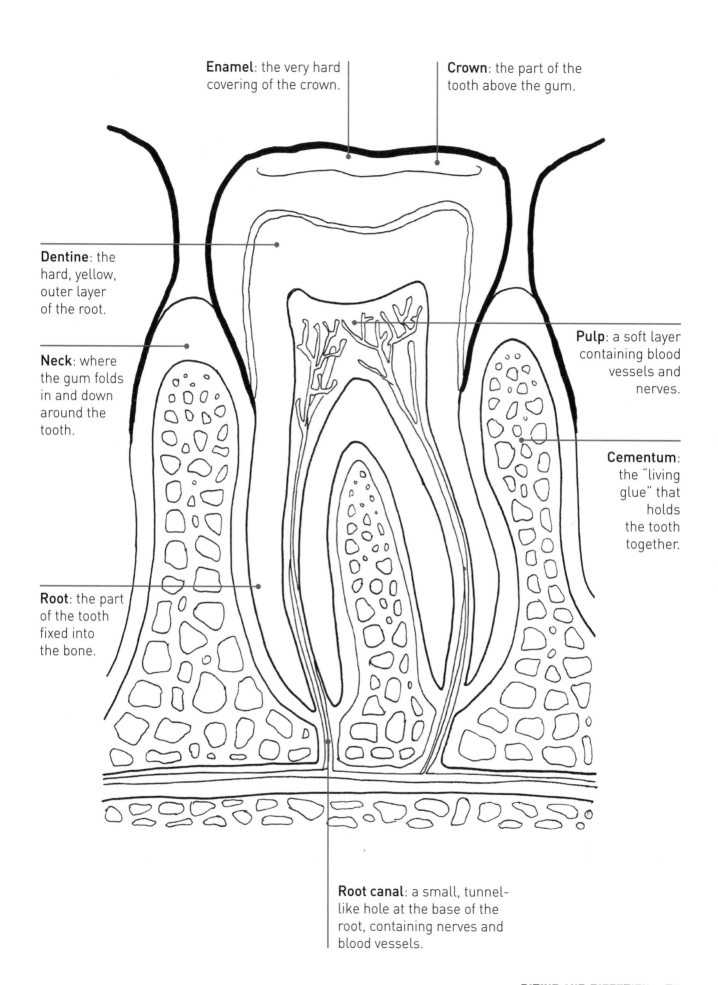

Enamel: the very hard covering of the crown.

Crown: the part of the tooth above the gum.

Dentine: the hard, yellow, outer layer of the root.

Neck: where the gum folds in and down around the tooth.

Root: the part of the tooth fixed into the bone.

Pulp: a soft layer containing blood vessels and nerves.

Cementum: the "living glue" that holds the tooth together.

Root canal: a small, tunnel-like hole at the base of the root, containing nerves and blood vessels.

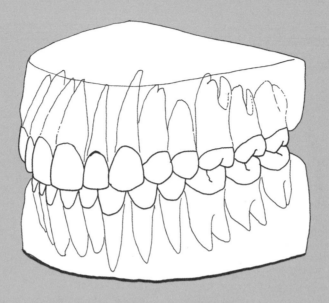

TWO SETS OF TEETH

Your first set of teeth are called milk teeth. They grow beneath the gum and have to force their way out. This process is called teething, and can be very painful. You only have 20 milk teeth.

Later another set of teeth forms in the gum, under the first set. This second set of teeth gradually push the milk teeth out until there are 32 permanent teeth.

QUICK FACTS

Babies are usually born without visible teeth, as they survive on **MILK** for the first few months of their lives.

However, their teeth have already started to grow beneath their **GUMS**.

Sometimes teeth grow **CROOKEDLY** in the mouth. This can be put right by wearing teeth braces.

Braces consist of metal or clear ceramic **BRACKETS** that are bonded onto the front surface of each tooth and connected by wires.

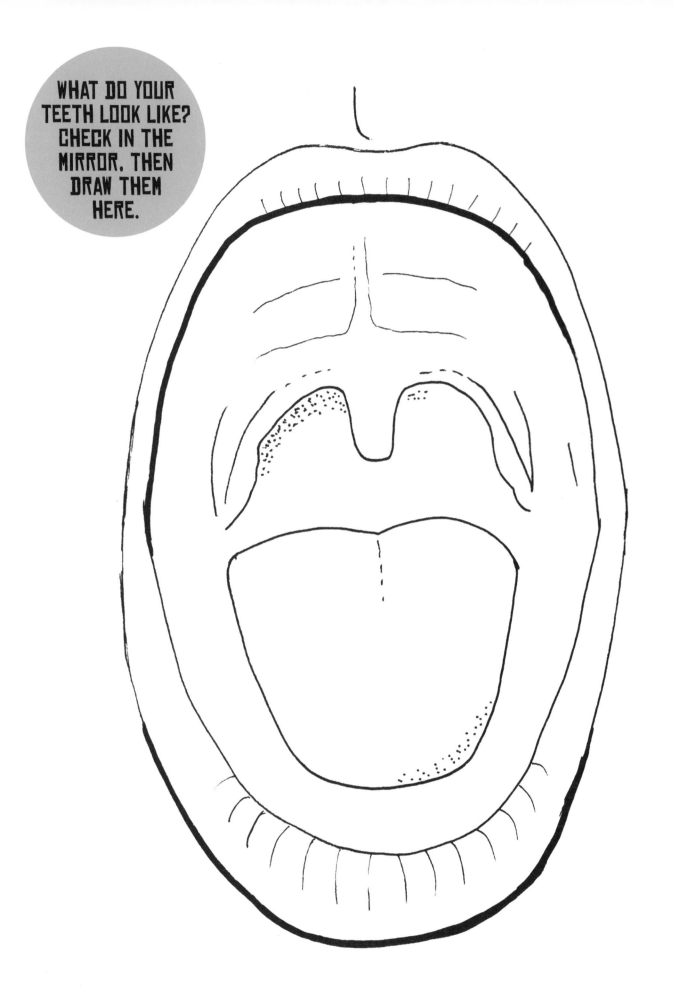

BRUSHING YOUR TEETH

Teeth are the hardest parts of the whole body. We use them hundreds of times each day as we bite and chew. But they are the only body parts that cannot mend themselves if they are damaged or diseased.

So we must look after them well, by brushing, flossing, and going for regular dental check-ups.

QUICK FACTS

Without proper brushing, **BACTERIA** will form on the hard enamel of the tooth.

The bacteria multiply and form a film over the enamel. This is called **PLAQUE**.

ACID in plaque makes tiny holes in the enamel. These get bigger and are called cavities.

The tooth does not hurt until the acid reaches the nerves. By then, the **CAVITY** is already there.

The average person spends around **35 DAYS** of their life brushing their teeth.

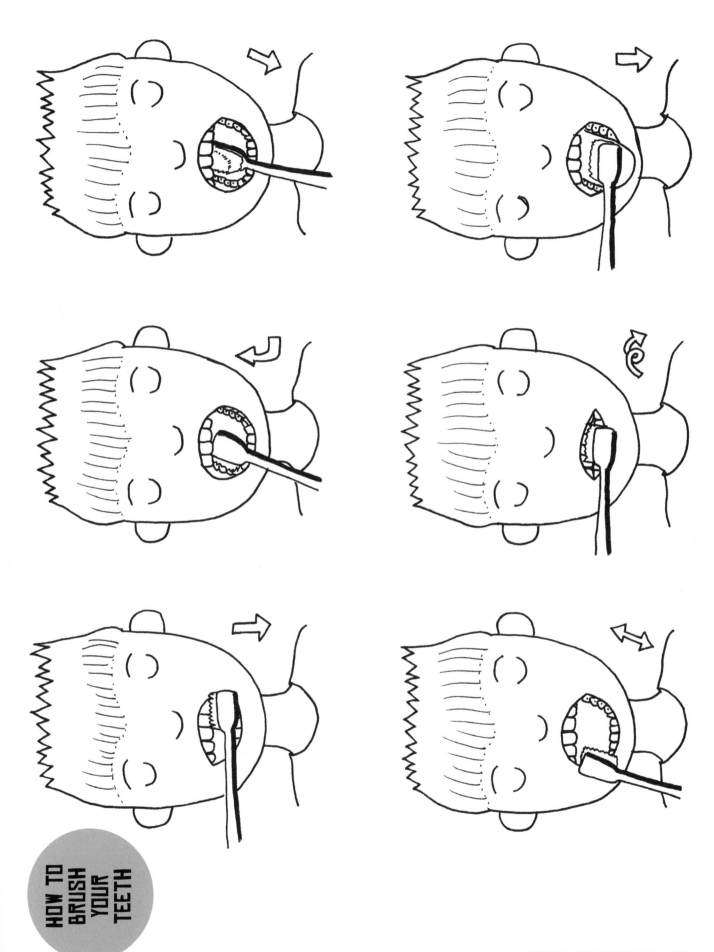

HOW TO BRUSH YOUR TEETH

DIGESTION

A car needs gasoline (petrol), a truck uses diesel, and a jet plane runs on kerosene. These are all fuels that provide the energy needed to make machines go. Your "body machine" needs fuel too, and it gets it in the form of food.

Digestion is the process of changing the food we eat so that it can be used by the body.

QUICK FACTS

The parts of the body specialized for taking in and breaking down foods into tiny pieces are called the **DIGESTIVE SYSTEM**.

The contents of your stomach are **CHURNED** about to mix the digestive juices throughout the food.

The digestive system makes more than 2.6 gallons of digestive **JUICES** each day.

Most of the **WATER** in these juices is taken back into the body by the large intestine.

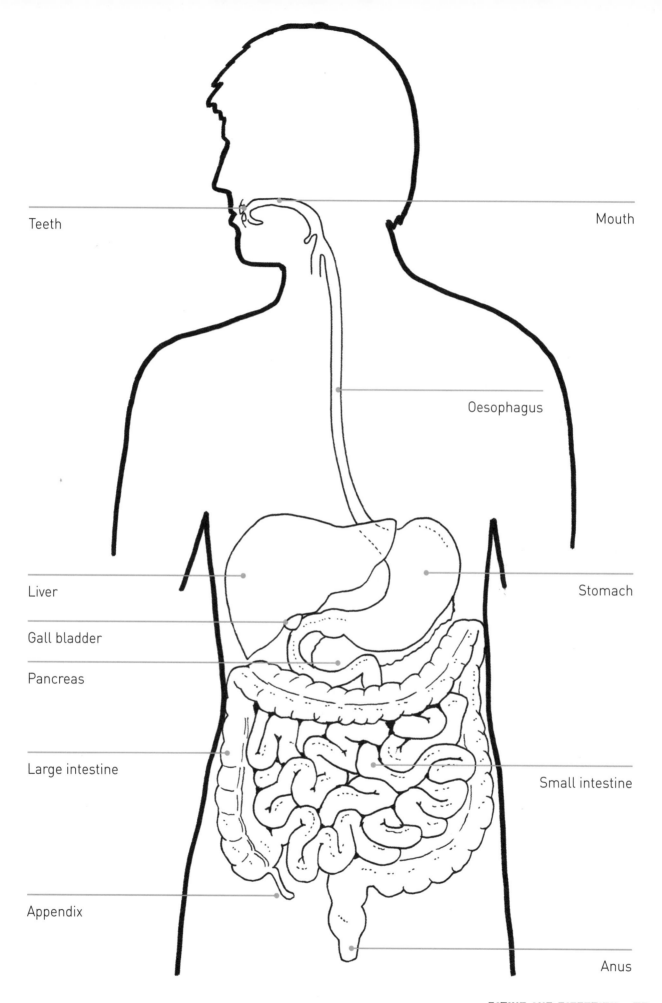

Teeth

Mouth

Oesophagus

Liver

Stomach

Gall bladder

Pancreas

Large intestine

Small intestine

Appendix

Anus

THE MOUTH

Digestion begins with the first bite. In your mouth the food is chopped up and chewed by your teeth and mixed with saliva.

Your tongue moistens and crushes your food and kneads it into a ball. This ball of food is then pushed down a short tube called the oesophagus to your stomach.

QUICK FACTS

The mouth is also known as the **ORAL CAVITY**.

Everyone's mouth is full of **BACTERIA**, although not all bacteria are harmful.

The **ROOF** of the mouth has two main parts. The front part behind the nose is called the hard palate, and the rear part above the back of the mouth is the soft palate.

The palate can **BEND UP** as a lump of food is pushed to the back of the mouth by swallowing.

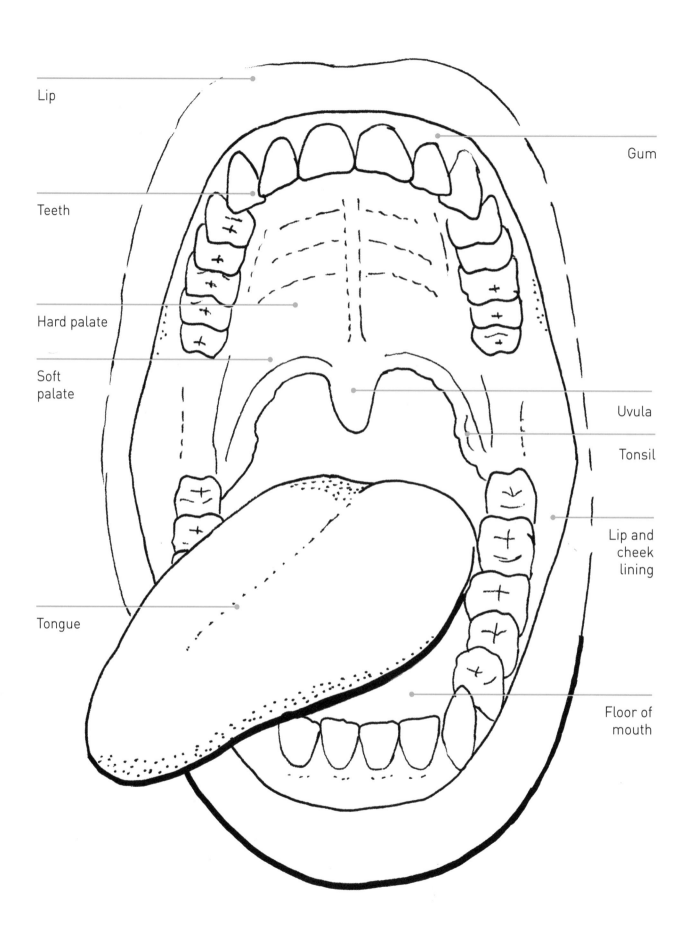

Lip

Teeth

Hard palate

Soft palate

Tongue

Gum

Uvula

Tonsil

Lip and cheek lining

Floor of mouth

SALIVA

Saliva keeps the mouth moist and comfortable when
we eat, and helps to moisten dry food, allowing it
to be chewed and swallowed more easily.

The mucus in saliva coats the bolus (or chewed food)
and acts as a lubricant to help us to swallow.

QUICK FACTS

Our taste sensors work less well when food is **DRY**,
so saliva gives food its taste.

Your salivary glands make a total of almost **FIVE PINTS**
of saliva each day.

Most of that is absorbed by **FOOD** as you chew it.

Saliva washes away small **PARTICLES** of food and helps
keep the mouth clean.

Saliva is also known as **SPIT**.

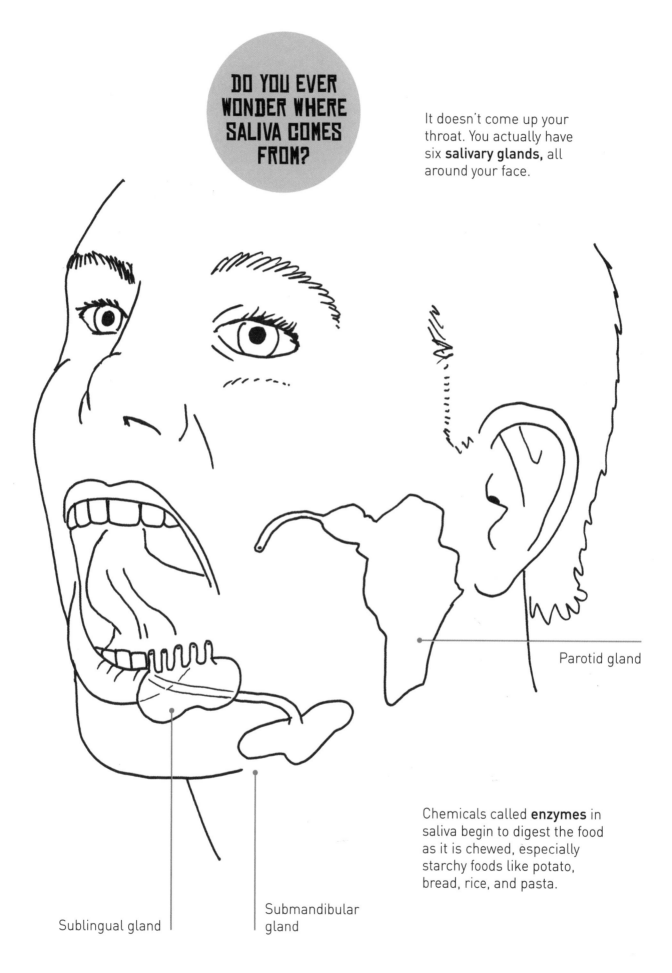

DO YOU EVER WONDER WHERE SALIVA COMES FROM?

It doesn't come up your throat. You actually have six **salivary glands,** all around your face.

Parotid gland

Chemicals called **enzymes** in saliva begin to digest the food as it is chewed, especially starchy foods like potato, bread, rice, and pasta.

Sublingual gland

Submandibular gland

THE THROAT

The "throat" is a term loosely applied to the part of the neck in front of the backbone. It contains structures important in breathing and eating.

As you swallow, your windpipe is closed by your epiglottis. This forces the food into its own passage, the oesophagus.

QUICK FACTS

Without the epiglottis, food would go into your windpipe, and you would **CHOKE**.

Your epiglottis is a leaf-shaped **FLAP** above your voice box.

Muscular **WAVES** carry food down your oesophagus to your stomach.

Many of the muscles you use for **TALKING** are also used for swallowing.

As you swallow

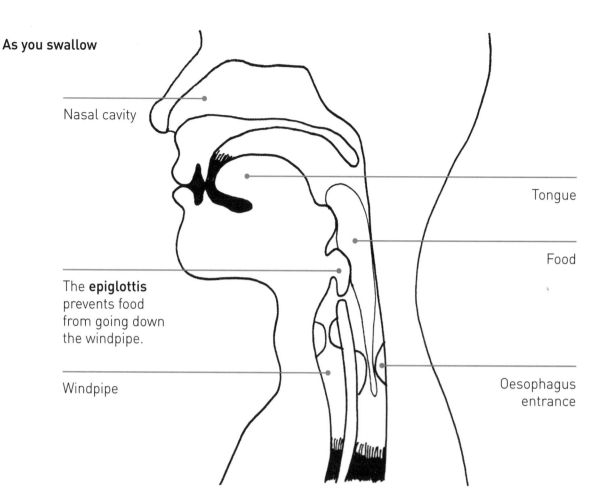

Nasal cavity

Tongue

Food

The **epiglottis** prevents food from going down the windpipe.

Windpipe

Oesophagus entrance

After the food has gone down

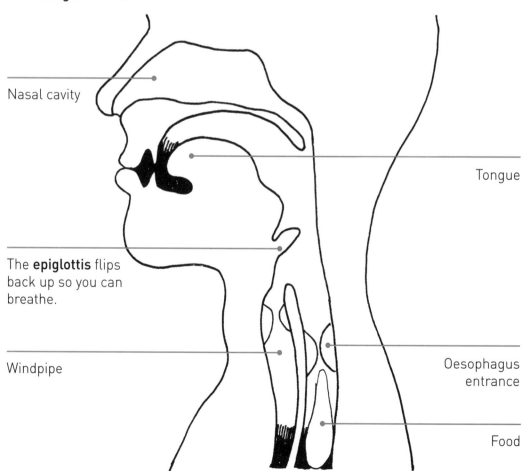

Nasal cavity

Tongue

The **epiglottis** flips back up so you can breathe.

Windpipe

Oesophagus entrance

Food

WATER

All cells, the basic units that make up all living things, contain water. Without it, life as we know it would be impossible.

As well as via drinking, water comes from so-called solid foods, such as fruit, vegetables, bread, and meat. Since these foods are also made up of cells they are not really dry but are 30–90 per cent water.

QUICK FACTS

During a day, an adult human being takes in about **5 PINTS** of water.

There are about 8.3 pints of **BLOOD** in the body, and 5 pints of this is water.

In addition to this, about 16.7 pints of water pass back and forth within the body between the various **ORGAN SYSTEMS** every day.

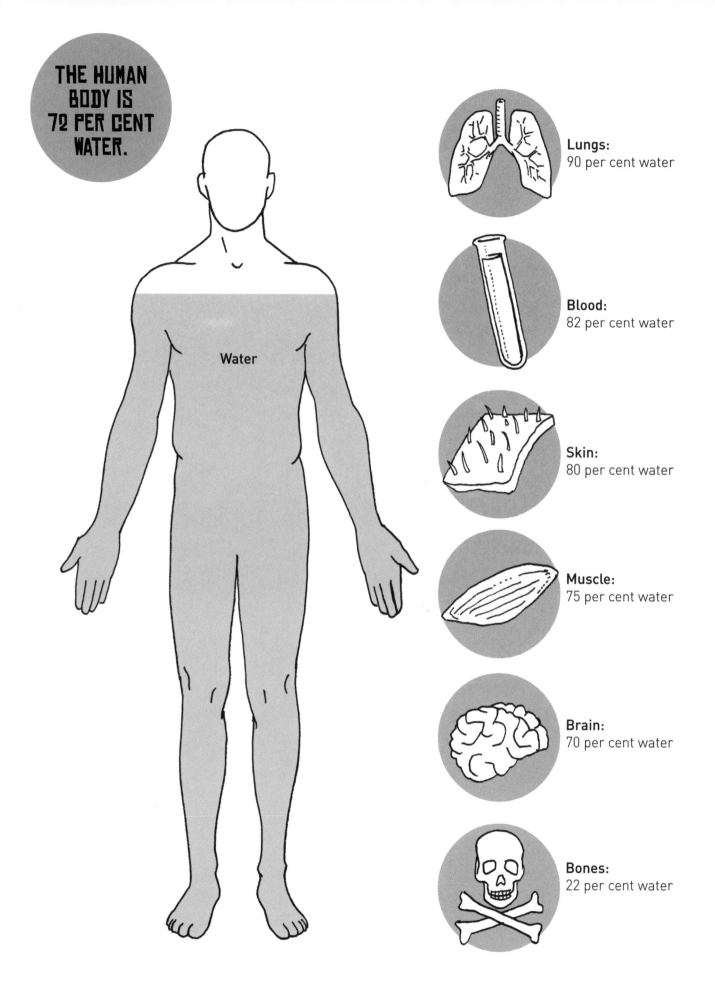

THE HUMAN BODY IS 72 PER CENT WATER.

Water

Lungs:
90 per cent water

Blood:
82 per cent water

Skin:
80 per cent water

Muscle:
75 per cent water

Brain:
70 per cent water

Bones:
22 per cent water

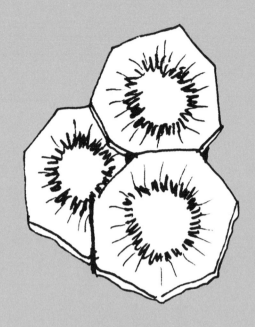

FOOD

We use one simple name for all the substances your body needs to take in: food.

However, in your food there are six main groups of material. They are: proteins, carbohydrates, fats, vitamins, minerals, and fiber.

QUICK FACTS

FATS are used for both building and energy.

CARBOHYDRATES are known as "energy foods".

FIBER is needed to help food to pass properly through the body.

PROTEINS provide some energy, but more importantly they serve as the main building materials of the body.

VITAMINS and **MINERALS** are a small but important part of your diet. There are many of them, and they each perform different roles.

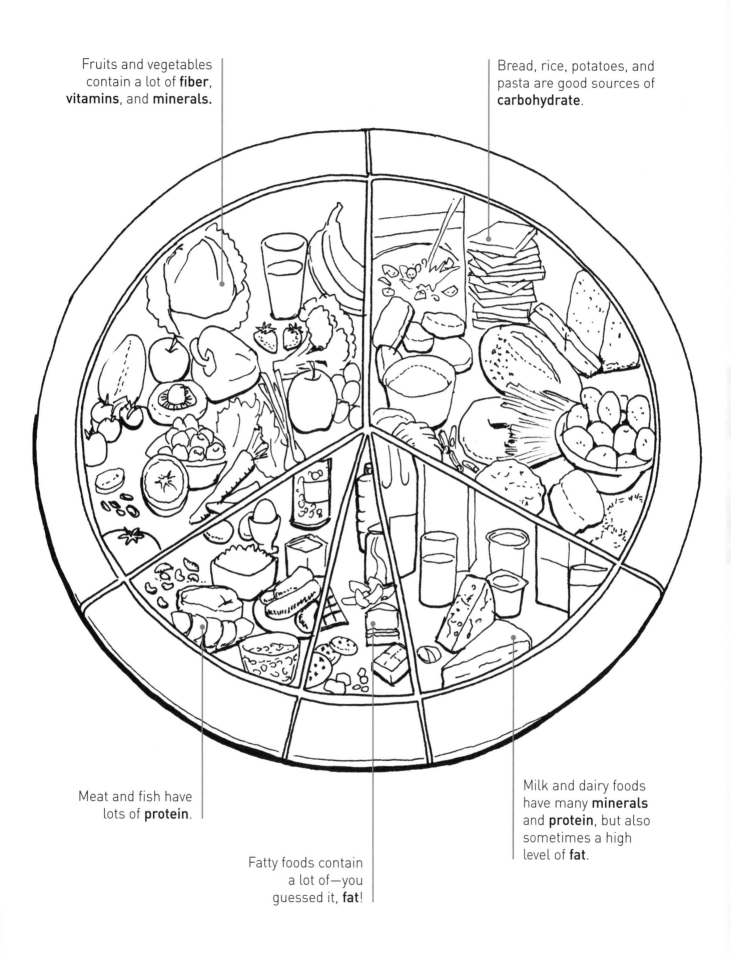

Fruits and vegetables contain a lot of **fiber**, **vitamins**, and **minerals**.

Bread, rice, potatoes, and pasta are good sources of **carbohydrate**.

Meat and fish have lots of **protein**.

Fatty foods contain a lot of—you guessed it, **fat**!

Milk and dairy foods have many **minerals** and **protein**, but also sometimes a high level of **fat**.

VITAMINS

We need chemicals known as vitamins in order to stay alive. They are named by giving them letters, such as vitamin A, vitamin B, and so on.

If you lack certain vitamins, you will get ill. For example, without enough vitamin C, your blood vessels become fragile and bleed easily. Black and blue marks appear on the skin and near the eyes.

Vitamin C can be found in citrus fruits and fresh vegetables.

QUICK FACTS

FRUITS contain a wide range of essential vitamins and minerals.

Some vitamins are **STORED** in the body, while others need to be eaten every day.

In the past, sailors who went on long trips and couldn't get **FRESH** vegetables would develop a disease called scurvy. In the 17th century, British sailors were given lemons and limes to prevent this disease.

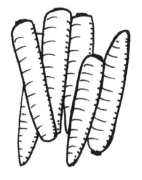

Carrots contain vitamin **A**.

Almonds contain vitamin **E**.

Spinach contains vitamin **K**.

Beans contain vitamin **B1**.

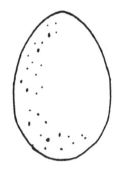

Eggs contain vitamin **B2**.

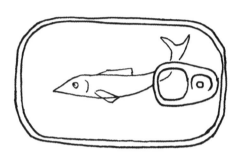

Sardines contain vitamin **B3**.

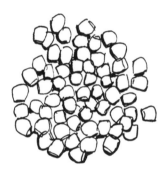

Sweetcorn contains
vitamin **A**.

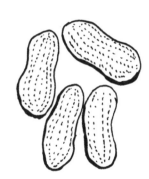

Peanuts contain vitamin **E**.

Bananas contain vitamin **K**.

Sunflower seeds contain
vitamin **B1**.

Prawns contain vitamin **B2**.

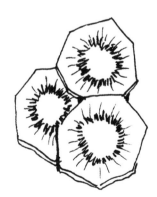

Kiwi fruit contain
vitamin **B3**.

FOOD'S JOURNEY

Food is pushed through your digestive system by waves of squeezing and relaxing muscles. This is called peristalsis.

In your oesophagus, peristalsis is so strong it even works if your body is upside down!

QUICK FACTS

The digestive system starts at the **MOUTH** and ends at the anus.

Without food inside, most of the digestive passageway would be squeezed **FLAT** by the natural pressure of other organs.

Food has to be pushed through the passageway by waves of muscle action in its walls, called **PERISTALSIS**.

In adults, the digestive system is about **29 FT** long.

Food can take anything from 10–20 hours to **PASS THROUGH** the system.

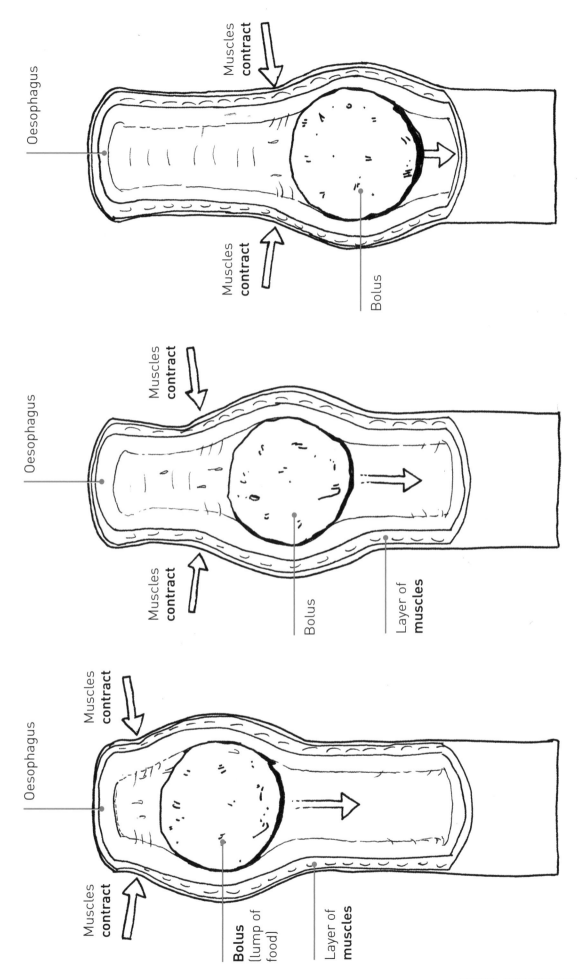

Oesophagus

Muscles **contract**

Muscles **contract**

Bolus

Oesophagus

Muscles **contract**

Muscles **contract**

Bolus

Layer of **muscles**

Oesophagus

Muscles **contract**

Muscles **contract**

Bolus (lump of food)

Layer of **muscles**

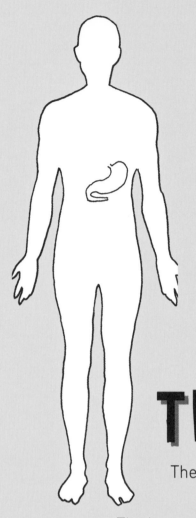

THE STOMACH

The stomach is like a stretchy storage bag for food. It expands to hold a whole meal.

The layers of muscle in its walls contract to make it squeeze first one way and then the other. Meanwhile, tiny glands in the stomach lining release their digestive chemicals.

After a few hours the food has become a mushy, part-digested soup.

QUICK FACTS

The stomach is a J-shaped **BAG** behind the left lower ribs.

Its lining makes thick **MUCUS** to protect the stomach's gastric juices from digesting the stomach itself.

An adult stomach can hold as much as **2.5 PINTS** of food.

If you did not have a stomach you could not eat just two or three main **MEALS** a day. You would have to eat lots of tiny ones much more frequently.

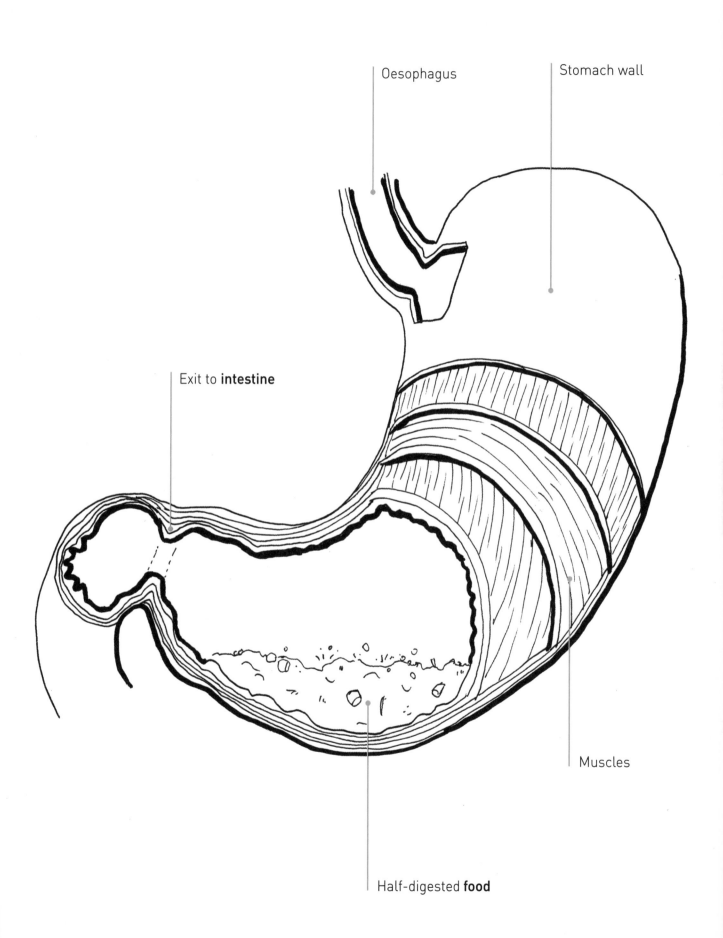

Oesophagus

Stomach wall

Exit to **intestine**

Muscles

Half-digested **food**

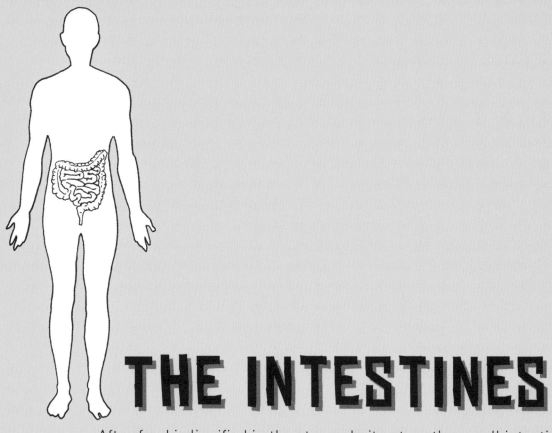

THE INTESTINES

After food is liquified in the stomach, it enters the small intestine.

In the first part of the small intestine, digestion continues. Juices from the pancreas and liver help to further break down the foods. It is also in the small intestine that digested food is absorbed into the blood and lymph.

Finally, in the large intestine, water is absorbed and the contents become more solid, so they can leave the body as waste material.

QUICK FACTS

The small intestine is about 7.6 yards long and is lined with small, finger-like nodules called **VILLI**.

Food particles are small enough to pass through the walls of the intestine and blood vessels only when they are completely **DIGESTED**.

Almost no digestion occurs in the large intestine. Its function is to **STORE** waste food products, and **ABSORB** water and small amounts of minerals.

The **WASTE** that accumulates in the large intestine is fibrous material that cannot be digested.

THERE ARE ABOUT 500 MILLION VILLI IN THE BODY.

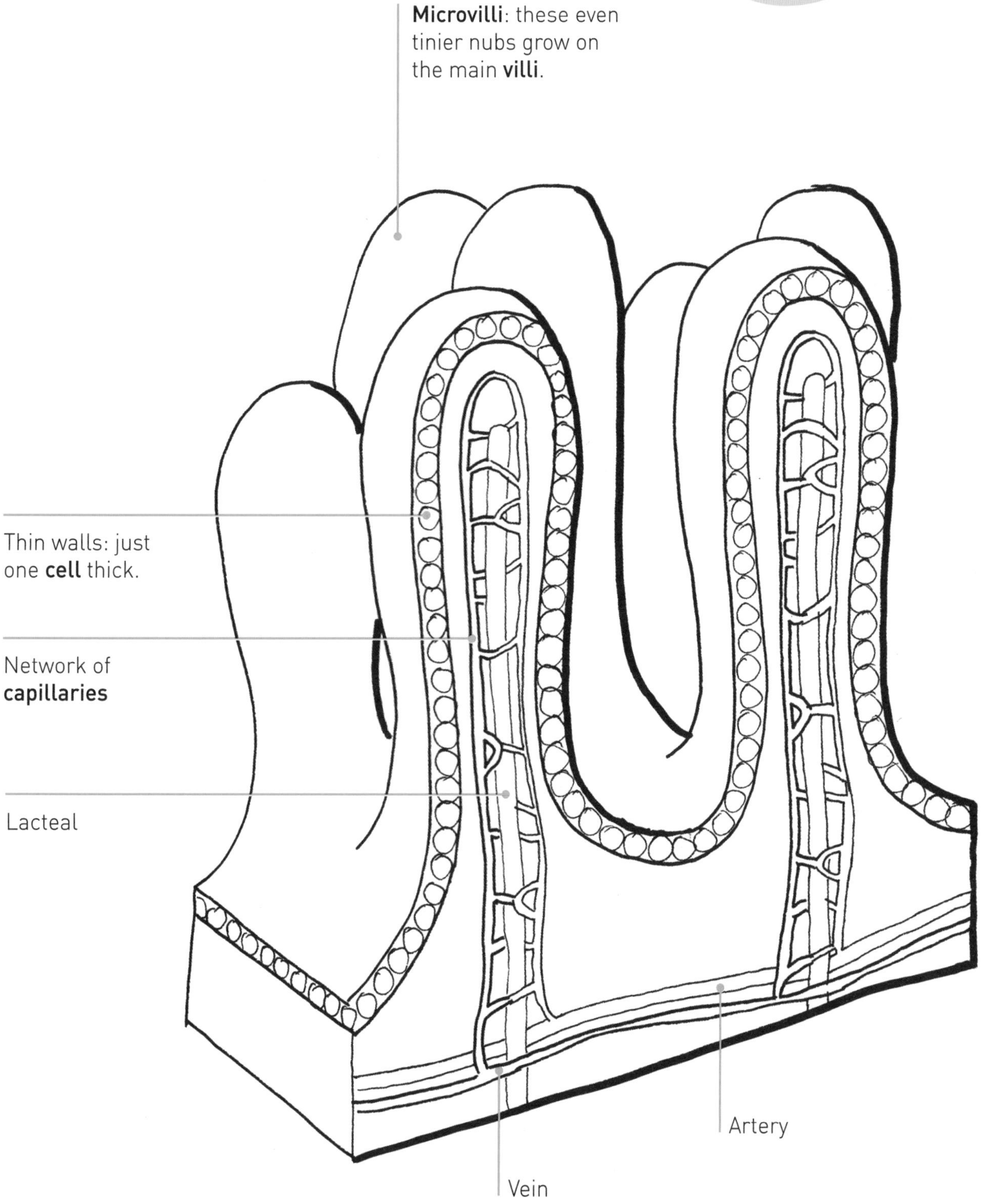
Microvilli: these even tinier nubs grow on the main **villi**.
Thin walls: just one **cell** thick.
Network of **capillaries**
Lacteal
Artery
Vein

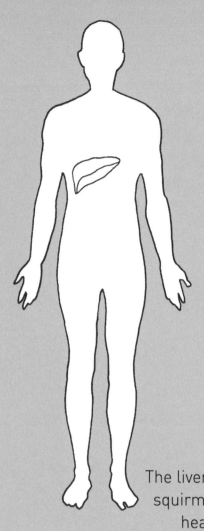

THE LIVER

The liver is one of the body's busiest parts. It does not squirm about or move, like the stomach, intestines, heart, or muscles. Its activities are invisible.

The liver has two key roles to play: making (or processing) new chemicals, and neutralizing poisons and waste products.

QUICK FACTS

The liver is the **LARGEST** single part, or organ, inside the body.

It plays an essential role in the **STORAGE** of certain vitamins.

The liver has more than 500 known **TASKS** in the body, and probably more that have not yet been discovered.

The liver is so busy with chemical processes and tasks that it makes lots of **HEAT**.

Usually the liver **BREAKS DOWN** old red blood cells and gets rid of the coloring substance in bile fluid.

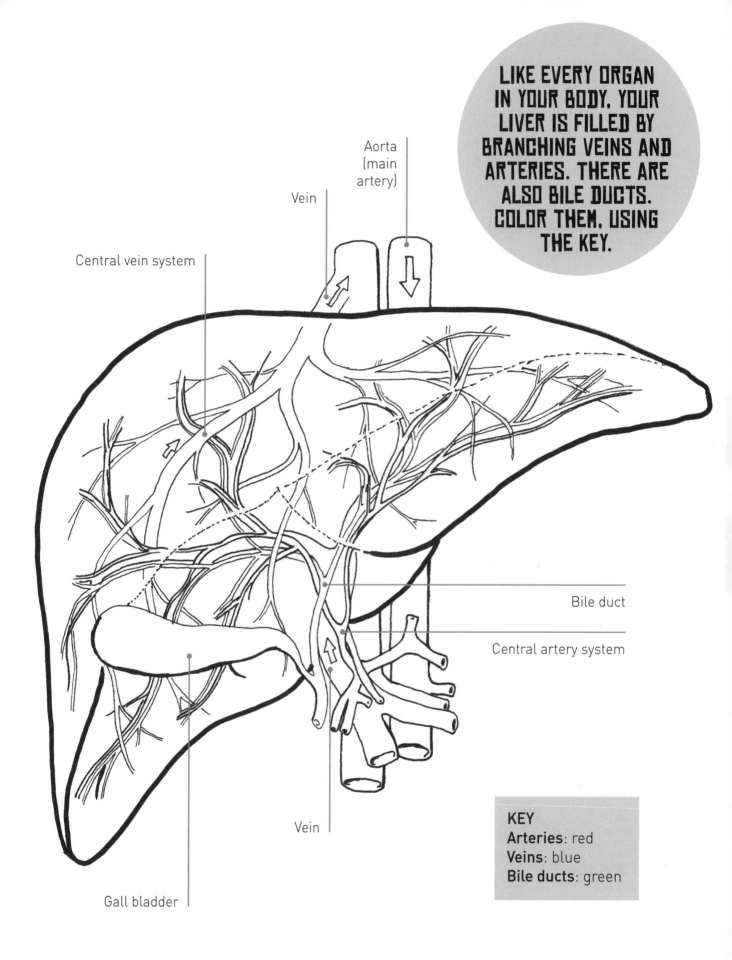

LIKE EVERY ORGAN IN YOUR BODY, YOUR LIVER IS FILLED BY BRANCHING VEINS AND ARTERIES. THERE ARE ALSO BILE DUCTS. COLOR THEM, USING THE KEY.

Vein

Aorta (main artery)

Central vein system

Bile duct

Central artery system

Vein

Gall bladder

KEY
Arteries: red
Veins: blue
Bile ducts: green

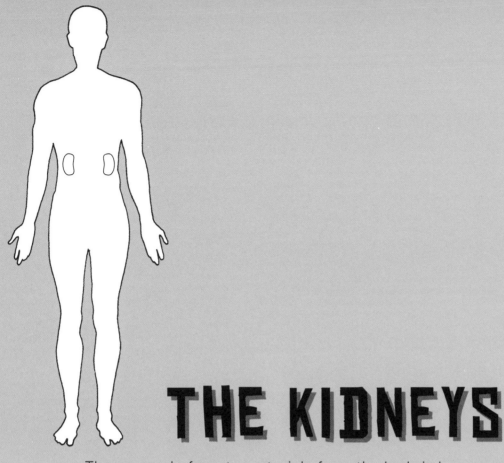

THE KIDNEYS

The removal of waste materials from the body is known as excretion, and the body's main organs of excretion are the kidneys.

Kidneys clean the blood by filtering out waste and straining off any water the body doesn't need. This liquid waste is called urine. It is stored in your bladder and then leaves your body when you go to the toilet.

QUICK FACTS

You have **TWO** kidneys, in the small of your back, one on either side of your backbone.

They look like large, reddish-brown **BEANS**, and each one is about the size of a clenched fist.

Your kidneys filter about **500 GALLONS** of blood daily.

The kidneys receive a **HUGE** blood supply through the renal arteries and veins.

The **ADRENAL GLANDS** are attached to the kidneys. They help create energy which stimulates the body to prepare it for instant action.

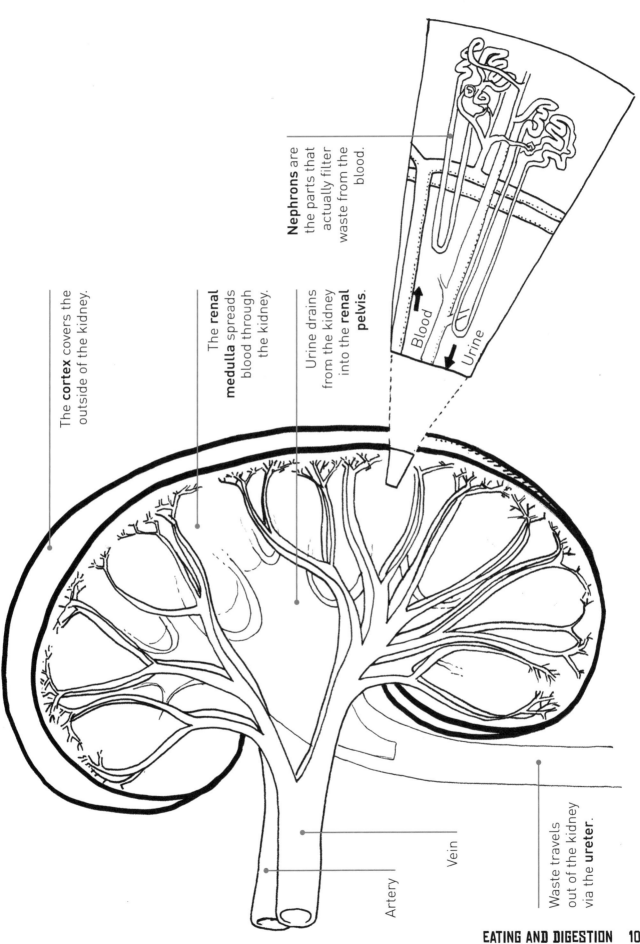

The **cortex** covers the outside of the kidney.

The **renal medulla** spreads blood through the kidney.

Urine drains from the kidney into the **renal pelvis**.

Nephrons are the parts that actually filter waste from the blood.

Blood

Urine

Artery

Vein

Waste travels out of the kidney via the **ureter**.

ENZYMES

An enzyme is a molecule that speeds up chemical reactions in all living things. Without enzymes, these reactions would occur too slowly or not at all, and no life would be possible.

The human body has thousands of kinds of enzymes. Each kind does one specific job.

QUICK FACTS

WITHOUT enzymes, a person could not breathe, see, move, or digest food!

Doctors **DIAGNOSE** some diseases by measuring the amount of various enzymes in blood and other body fluids.

Such **DISEASES** include anaemia, cancer, leukaemia, and heart and liver ailments.

Some **DETERGENTS** contain enzymes that break down protein or fats that cause stains.

In the future, enzymes may also be used to help get rid of spilled **OIL** that harms lakes and oceans. The enzymes would turn the oil into food for sea plants.

Chemical molecule
(reactant)

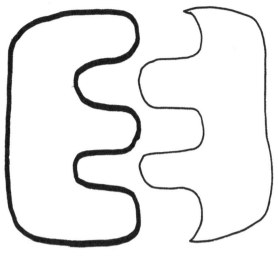

Enzyme molecule

ENZYMES TAKE IN ONE KIND OF CHEMICAL, AND CHANGE IT INTO ANOTHER. DIFFERENT KINDS OF ENZYMES HANDLE DIFFERENT CHEMICALS.

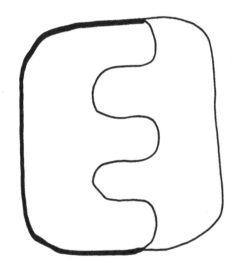

Enzyme and reactant **combine** for a short time.

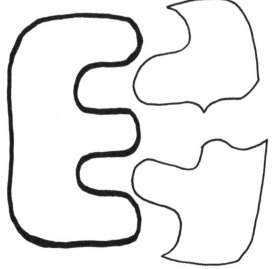

The enzyme is **unchanged** by the reaction.

The reactant is **broken** into two molecules.

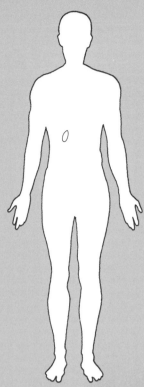

THE GALL BLADDER

The gall bladder is a small bag that contains a yellowish fluid called bile.

The liver makes up to a quart of bile every day. Some of this stays in the liver and some in the gall bladder—that is until you have a meal. Then bile flows from the gall bladder and liver to a tube called the common bile duct, which empties into the small intestine.

QUICK FACTS

BILE is a waste product from the liver.

It also helps with **DIGESTION**, by breaking apart the fats and oils in foods.

The gall bladder can **HOLD** about 1.5 fluid ounces of bile at any one time.

Sometimes the gall bladder gets filled with **GALLSTONES**, hard lumps that are on average the size of a pea.

They can be removed by **SURGERY** or smashed by very high-pitched sound waves called ultrasound.

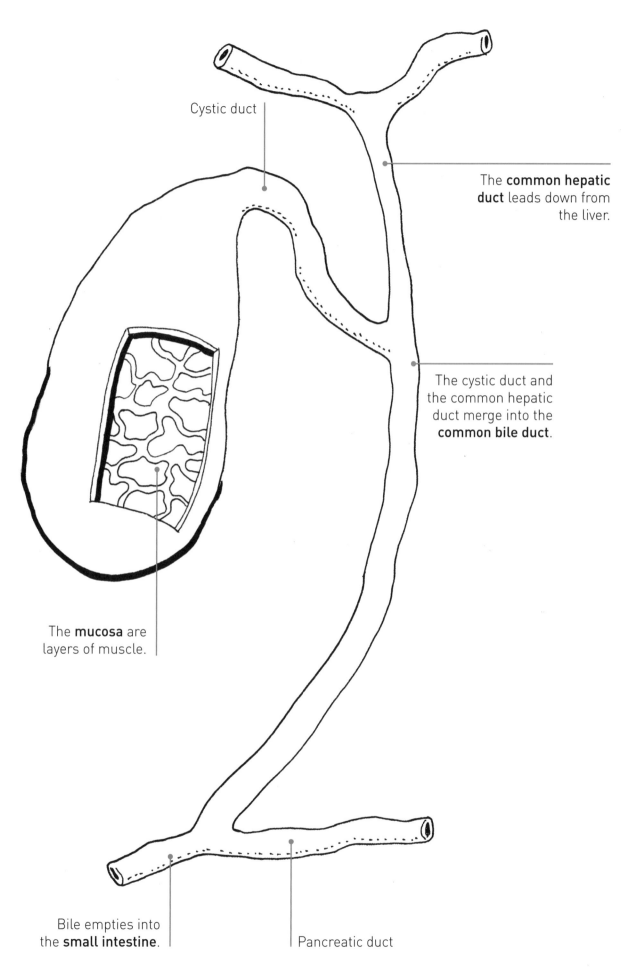

Cystic duct

The **common hepatic duct** leads down from the liver.

The cystic duct and the common hepatic duct merge into the **common bile duct**.

The **mucosa** are layers of muscle.

Bile empties into the **small intestine**.

Pancreatic duct

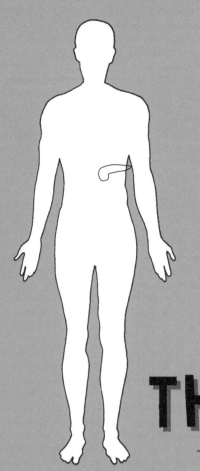

THE PANCREAS

The pancreas is a long, slim, wedge- or triangular-shaped part. It has two main jobs. One is to make hormones, the other is to make digestive chemicals called pancreatic juices.

During a meal, these pass along the pancreatic duct tubes into the small intestine to attack and digest foods there. Fatty foods, such as chips, are broken apart by enzymes made in the pancreas.

QUICK FACTS

The pancreas is one of the largest **GLANDS** in the body.

It makes **HORMONES** such as insulin, which controls the amount of sugar you have in your blood.

The pancreas makes about 2.6 pints of **DIGESTIVE JUICES** daily.

These juices contain about 15 powerful **ENZYMES** that break apart many substances in foods, including proteins, carbohydrates, and fats.

The pancreas is about **6 IN.** long.

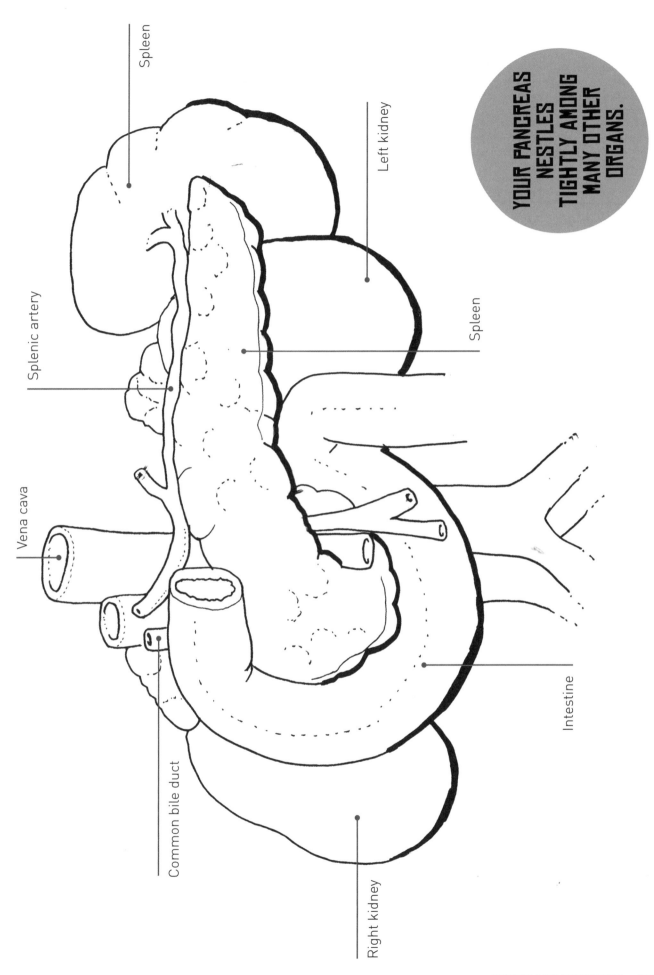

Spleen

Left kidney

Spleen

Splenic artery

Vena cava

Common bile duct

Right kidney

Intestine

YOUR PANCREAS NESTLES TIGHTLY AMONG MANY OTHER ORGANS.

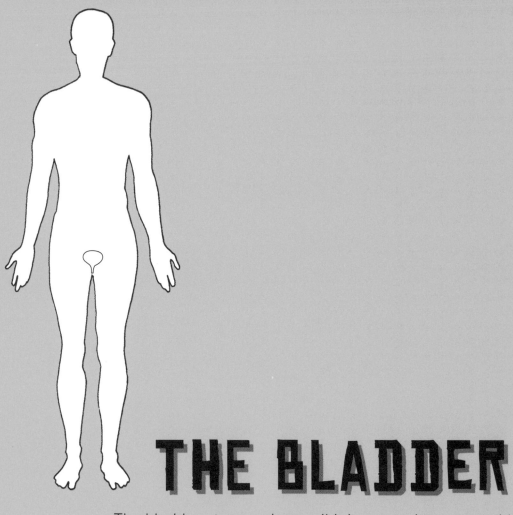

THE BLADDER

The bladder stores urine until it is convenient to get rid of it.
When empty, the bladder is pear-shaped and not much bigger than a thumb.
It gradually stretches and fills with urine until you feel the need to empty it.

Urine drains continuously from the kidneys into the
bladder through two tubes called ureters.

QUICK FACTS

The bladder can hold more than a **PINT** of urine.

We can tell how much urine is inside the bladder by how
much we need to **URINATE**.

When you eat lots of meat, your urine gets darker.
This is because your body makes urea, which gives
urine its color, from **PROTEINS**.

Men and women have different **SYSTEMS** for taking
urine to the outside of the body.

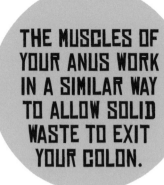

THE MUSCLES OF YOUR ANUS WORK IN A SIMILAR WAY TO ALLOW SOLID WASTE TO EXIT YOUR COLON.

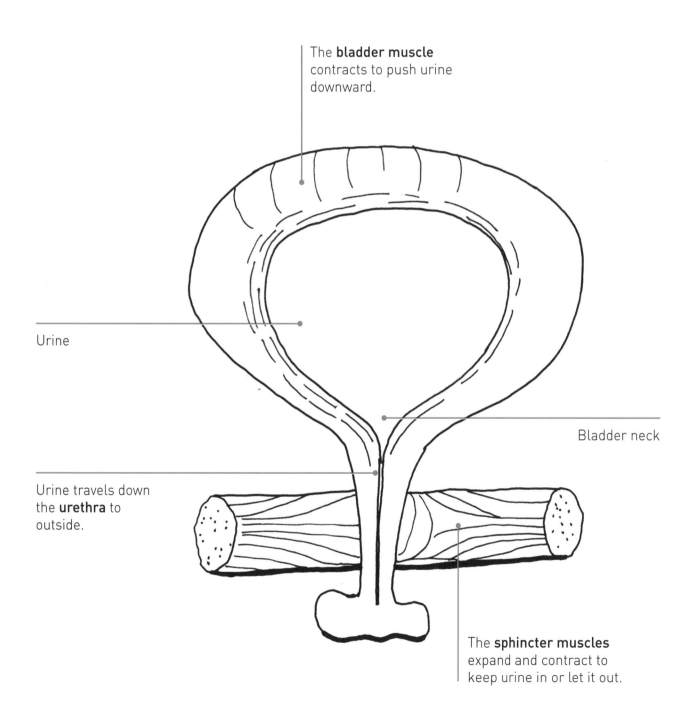

The **bladder muscle** contracts to push urine downward.

Urine

Bladder neck

Urine travels down the **urethra** to outside.

The **sphincter muscles** expand and contract to keep urine in or let it out.

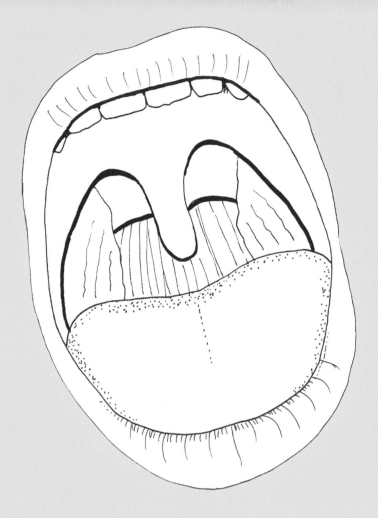

THE TONSILS

No one really knows the purpose of tonsils, but many medical scientists believe they aid in protecting the respiratory and digestive systems from infection.

QUICK FACTS

Your tonsils are found at the sides of the throat, just below and on either side of the soft **PALATE**.

They consist of a gathering of small **LYMPH NODES** called nodules.

They help to kill **GERMS** in breathed-in air, and also in foods and drinks.

They **SWELL UP** when battling illness, causing a sore throat. They may need removing if this happens often.

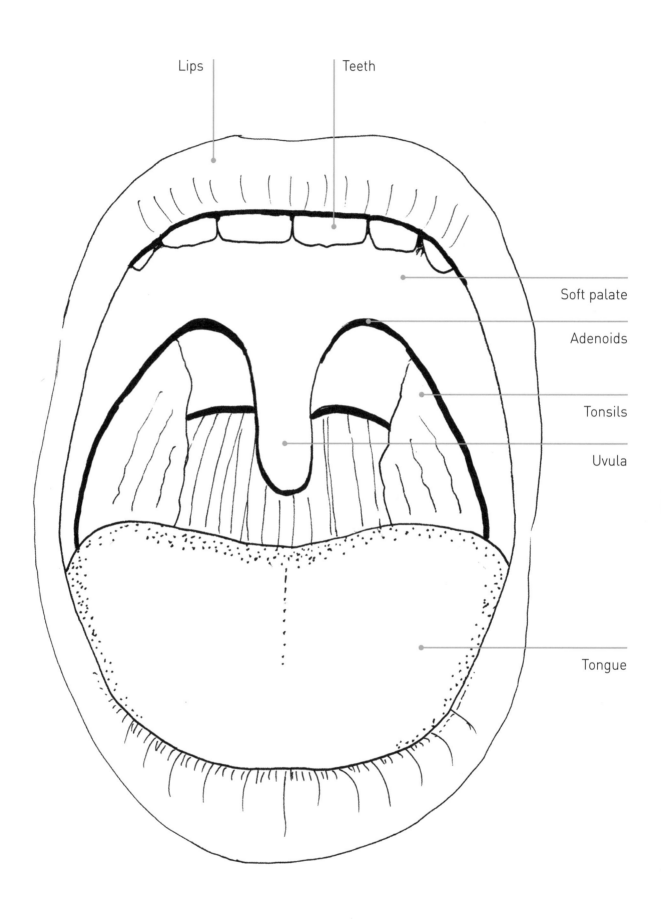

Lips

Teeth

Soft palate

Adenoids

Tonsils

Uvula

Tongue

SENSES

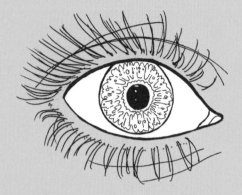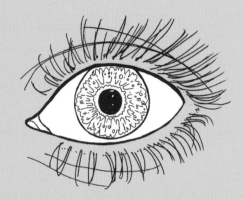

THE EYES

The eye is very like a camera. It has an adjustable opening to let in the light (the pupil), a lens that focuses the light to form an image, and a sensitive film (the retina) on which the image is recorded.

Inside each human eye are about 130 billion light-sensitive cells. When light falls on one of these cells it causes a chemical change. This change starts an impulse in the eye fiber which sends a message through the optic nerve to the "seeing" part of your brain.

QUICK FACTS

The human eye is so **SENSITIVE** that a person sitting on top of a hill on a moonless night could see a match being struck up to 50 miles away.

BIRDS have the keenest sight of all animals, including human beings. An osprey can see a dead animal on the ground from a height of up to 20 miles.

Each **EYEBALL** sits in a bony bowl called the eye socket. It is formed by curved parts of five skull bones.

The eye is one of the body parts that **GROWS** least from birth to adulthood.

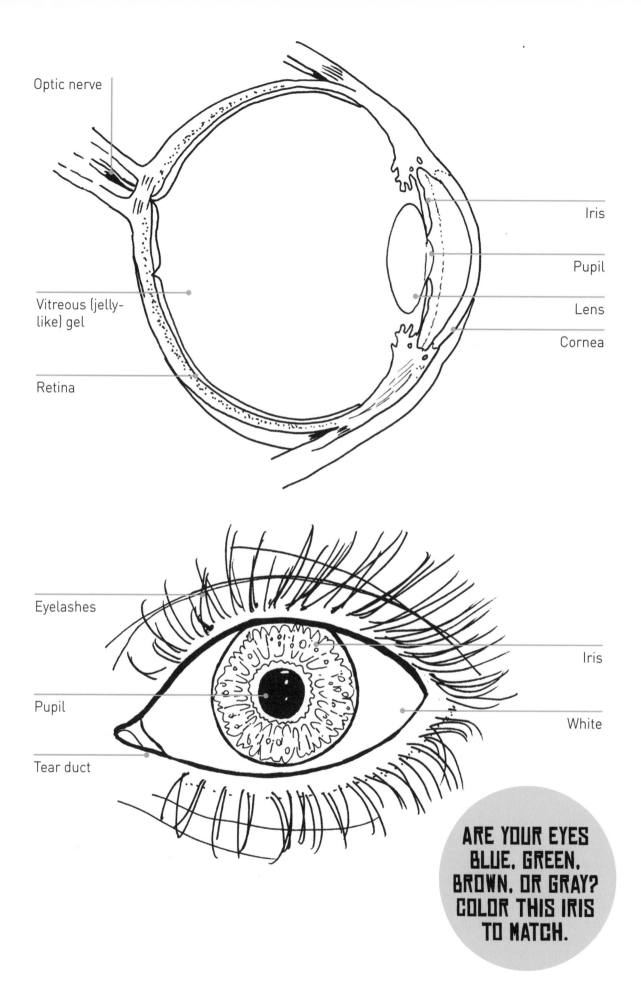

Optic nerve

Iris

Pupil

Vitreous (jelly-like) gel

Lens

Cornea

Retina

Eyelashes

Iris

Pupil

White

Tear duct

ARE YOUR EYES BLUE, GREEN, BROWN, OR GRAY? COLOR THIS IRIS TO MATCH.

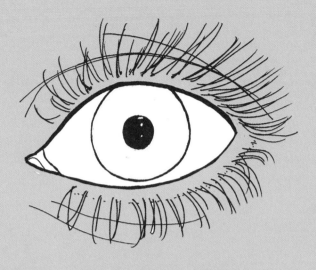

IRIS AND PUPIL

The iris is a colored ring of muscle that can alter the size of the hole (the pupil) within it, making it smaller in bright light to protect the delicate inside of the eye.

In the middle of the iris is the pupil, which looks like a black circle. The size of the pupil regulates the amount of light that enters the eye. Two muscles in the iris automatically adjust the size of the pupil to the level of light.

QUICK FACTS

Each person has irises of a different color, with a different, detailed, **PATTERN** of marks.

Scans of your iris can be used like fingerprints for **IDENTIFICATION** and security checks.

Occasionally, a person has two **DIFFERENT-COLORED** irises. They may have been born like that, or suffered an injury or illness.

Usually, people with lighter skin and hair have **BLUER** irises. People with darker skin and hair have **BROWNER** irises.

EVERY IRIS HAS ITS OWN INTRICATE PATTERN. DRAW DIFFERENT PATTERNS ON EACH OF THESE IRISES, THEN COLOR THEM IN.

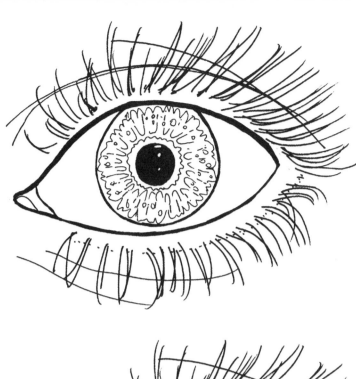

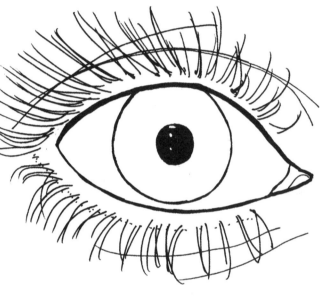

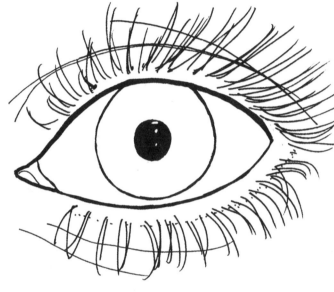

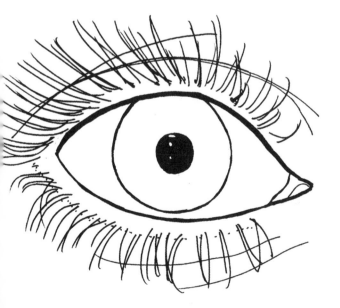

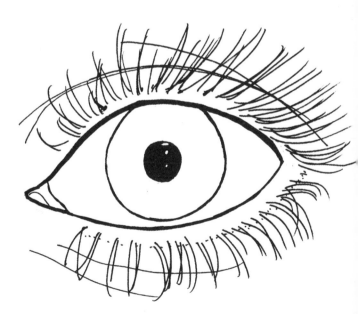

COLOR VISION

The retina of the eye is packed with a layer of tiny cells called rods and cones. These cells contain colored substances that react when light falls on them, triggering a nerve impulse.

QUICK FACTS

Each of your eyes has 125 million **ROD** cells and 7 million **CONE** cells. They detect light.

The rod and cone receptor cells are buried in the **RETINA**.

The mass of rod and cone cells in our eyes is like an organized network of electrical **WIRING**.

In some people, not all of these cones are present or work properly. This is called "**COLOR BLINDNESS**".

True color blindness is when people cannot see any color at all, but this is very **RARE**.

The most common form is when **RED** and **GREEN** appear similar.

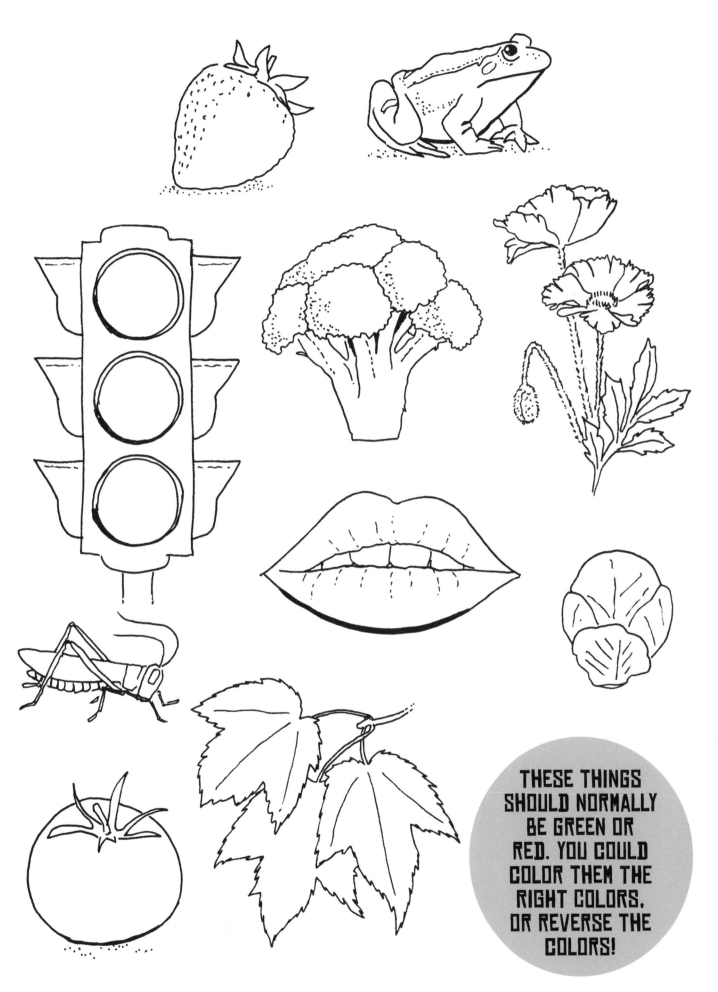

THESE THINGS SHOULD NORMALLY BE GREEN OR RED. YOU COULD COLOR THEM THE RIGHT COLORS, OR REVERSE THE COLORS!

TEARS

Tear fluid comes from the lachrymal gland, just above and to the outer side of each eye, under a fold of skin. It helps to clear the eye of foreign particles, such as dust and hairs, and keep it from drying out, which would result in blindness.

When a person feels some emotion very strongly, such as grief or anger, the muscles around the lacrymal glands may tighten up and squeeze out the tear fluid. The same thing happens if a person laughs very heartily.

QUICK FACTS

ONIONS contain an oil that irritates the eye. The eye reacts by blinking and producing tears to wash it away. That is why we cry when we chop onions.

After crying, a person may have to **BLOW** their nose to clear the drainage system of excess tears.

Lacrymal fluid also contains substances that fight **BACTERIA**, and proteins that help make the eye immune to infection.

On average, you **BLINK** six times per minute.

A blink **LASTS** about 0.3 seconds.

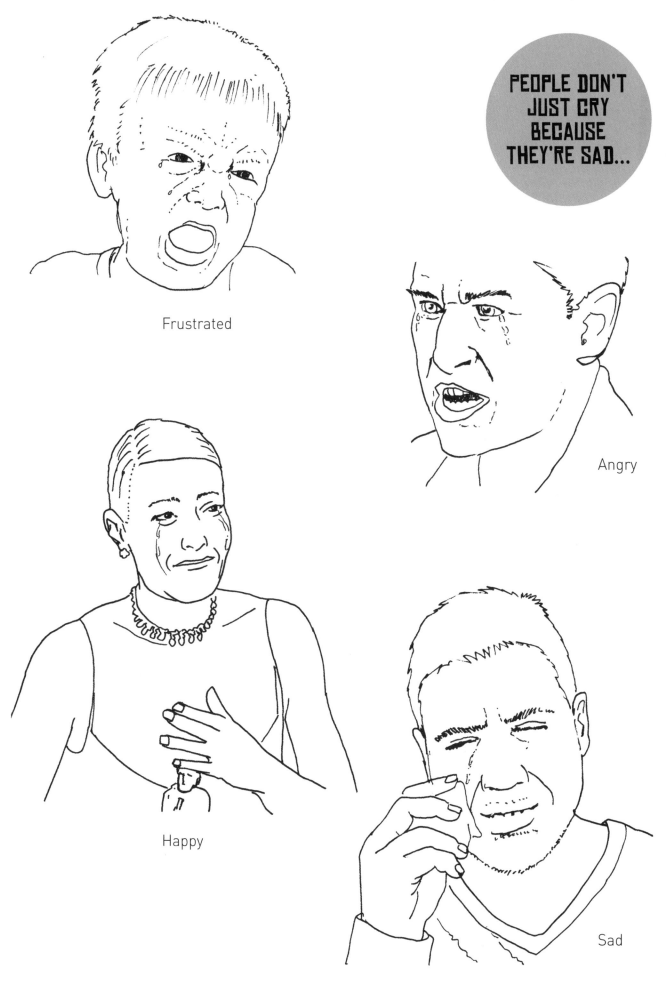

Frustrated

Angry

Happy

Sad

PEOPLE DON'T JUST CRY BECAUSE THEY'RE SAD...

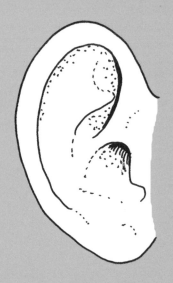

THE EARS

Hearing involves much more than the ears on the side of your head. These are the outer ears or ear flaps, made of skin-covered cartilage. The inner ear is deep in the temporal skull bone, almost behind the eye.

The ear is actually made up of three parts: outer, middle, and inner.

QUICK FACTS

When you fly in a plane your ears may **POP** as the air inside them expands. Otherwise, your eardrum would burst as the air trapped inside your ear expanded.

The middle and inner ears are **PROTECTED** from knocks by skull bones.

A sound from **ONE SIDE** reaches the ear on that side more than 1,000th of a second before it reaches the other ear.

The brain "**BLOCKS OUT**" frequent noise like humming machinery. Only when we hear something **NEW** does the mind turn its attention to hearing.

We never see lightning and hear **THUNDER** at the same time. This is because light travels faster than sound.

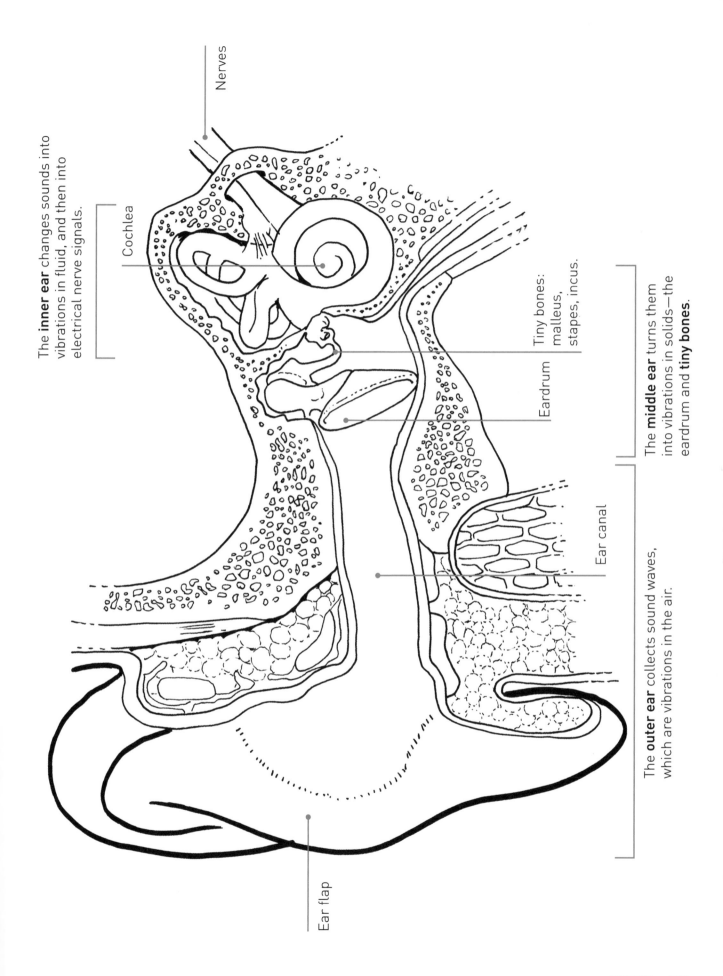

Nerves

The **inner ear** changes sounds into vibrations in fluid, and then into electrical nerve signals.

Cochlea

Tiny bones: malleus, stapes, incus.

Eardrum

The **middle ear** turns them into vibrations in solids—the eardrum and **tiny bones**.

Ear canal

The **outer ear** collects sound waves, which are vibrations in the air.

Ear flap

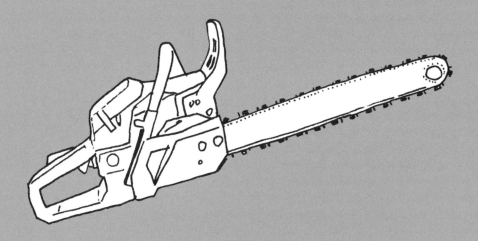

QUIET AND LOUD

If a sound is too quiet, we cup our hands around our ear flaps to help direct the sound waves into our inner ear. If it's too loud, we put our hands over our ears to try to protect them.

Some sounds are too loud for us to hear comfortably. Very loud noises can even tear the eardrum and cause partial or complete deafness.

QUICK FACTS

Loud noises make the **EARDRUM** tighten, pulling the stirrup bone away from the cochlea in order to protect the inner ear.

The loudness of a sound is measured in **DECIBELS** (dB).

Sounds **ABOVE 90 DB**, especially if high-pitched like whining or sawing, can damage hearing.

Many places, such as factories, airports, and music clubs, have **LAWS** controlling noise.

0 dB Total silence

10 dB Lower limit of human hearing

20 dB Watch ticking

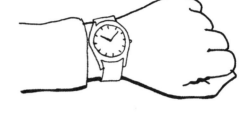

30 dB Whisper

40 dB Quiet talking, distant traffic

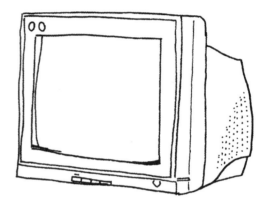

50 dB Normal talking

60 dB Normal television volume

70 dB Traffic in city street, vacuum cleaner

80 dB Alarm clock ringing, nearby truck

90 dB Heavy traffic at side of motorway, music in disco or club

100 dB Chainsaw, road drill

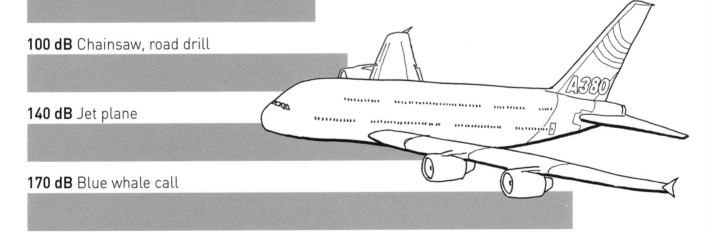

140 dB Jet plane

170 dB Blue whale call

200 dB Atomic explosion

THE NOSE

As you breathe in, air passes through a cavity behind your nose, which contains patches of millions of smell receptors. Sensory hairs stick out from the surface of these cells. The hairs detect smells and pass information along nerve fibers to the brain.

Substances that you can recognize as having an odor dissolve in the layer of mucus covering the sensory cells, stimulating them to produce a signal.

QUICK FACTS

The little hairs in the nose also **CLEAN** the air we inhale, as well as warming it before it enters the body.

The **OLFACTORY** (smelling) patch in the top of the nasal chamber has about the same area as a thumbnail.

Most people are able to detect about **4,000** different smells.

People whose work is based on their ability to smell, such as chefs, perfume makers, and wine tasters, can distinguish as many as **10,000** different smells.

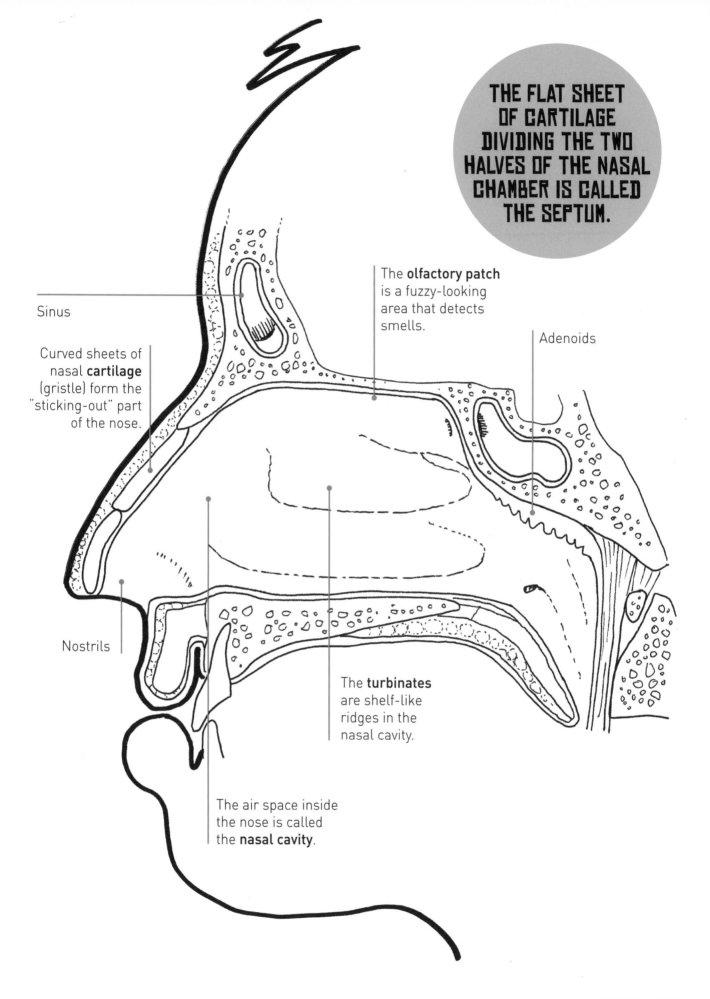

Sinus

The **olfactory patch** is a fuzzy-looking area that detects smells.

Adenoids

Curved sheets of nasal **cartilage** (gristle) form the "sticking-out" part of the nose.

Nostrils

The **turbinates** are shelf-like ridges in the nasal cavity.

The air space inside the nose is called the **nasal cavity**.

SMELL

The part of the brain that analyzes messages coming from the receiver cells in the nose is closely connected with the part of the brain that deals with emotions, moods, and memory.

The connection explains why smells have emotional significance. The smell of fresh rain on a summer's day usually makes people feel happy and invigorated, and it may also evoke happy memories.

QUICK FACTS

Unpleasant smells such as rotten eggs produce **REVULSION** and sometimes even nausea.

If we were to lose our sense of smell, almost all **TASTE** sensation would be lost as well, meaning that we would not enjoy the taste of our food nearly so much.

The human sense of smell is very **POOR** compared to that of animals, such as dogs.

Some **DOGS** are able to identify and follow the smell of a person's perspiration.

AROMATHERAPY is the art of using the perfumed essential oils of plants to treat the body and mind. The perfume passes over the nerve cells in the nasal passage and a message is sent to the brain.

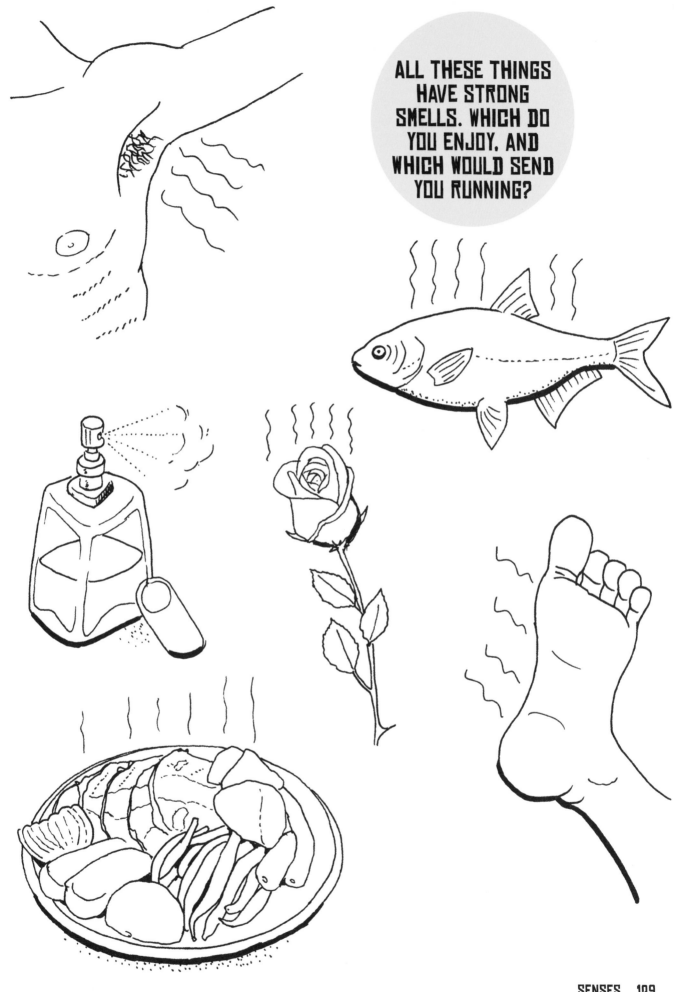

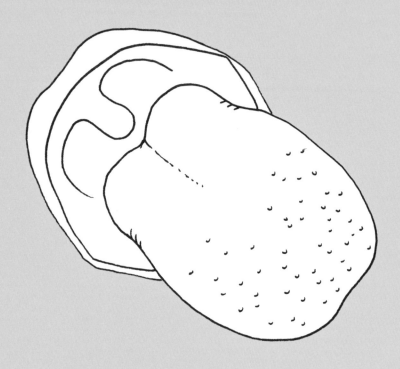

THE TONGUE

The tongue is the body's most flexible muscle. It has 12 sections of muscles inside it, and goes from long and thin, when poking out, to short and wide at the back of the mouth, in less than a second.

The tongue helps with chewing and swallowing, and also with the formation of words.

QUICK FACTS

We sense different basic **FLAVORS** on different parts of the tongue.

The four main **TASTES** are sweet, salt, sour, and bitter.

You can **CHECK** where the four tastes are by dabbing your tongue with a little salt, sugar, coffee grounds (bitter), and lemon juice (sour).

A fifth taste, **UMAMI**, has also been recognized in recent years, and relates to the Japanese word for "savory".

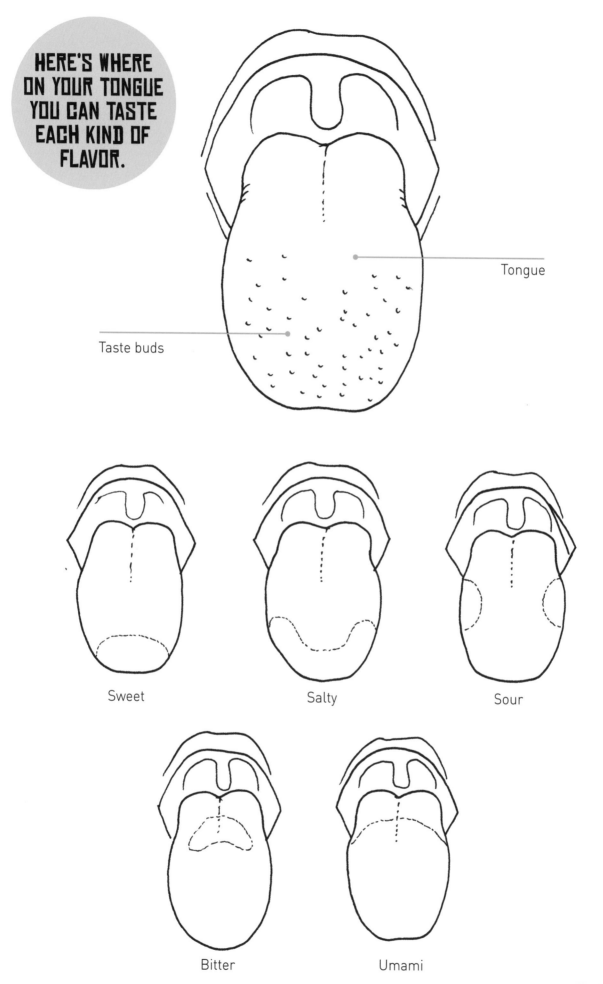

HERE'S WHERE ON YOUR TONGUE YOU CAN TASTE EACH KIND OF FLAVOR.

Tongue

Taste buds

Sweet

Salty

Sour

Bitter

Umami

THE TASTE BUDS

Taste buds grow in small nubs on your tongue, called papillae.

The underside of your tongue is smooth, but the papillae give the top of it a rough surface.

Each papilla contains one to two hundred taste buds.

QUICK FACTS

Each taste bud is **TINY**: a microscopic bunch of about 50 cells which have furry, frilly tips.

We each have around 10,000 **TASTE BUDS** on our tongue.

The sense of taste is the **CRUDEST** of our five senses. It is limited in both range and versatility.

When we eat **SPICY** foods, such as curry or chili, mild pain also forms a part of the taste.

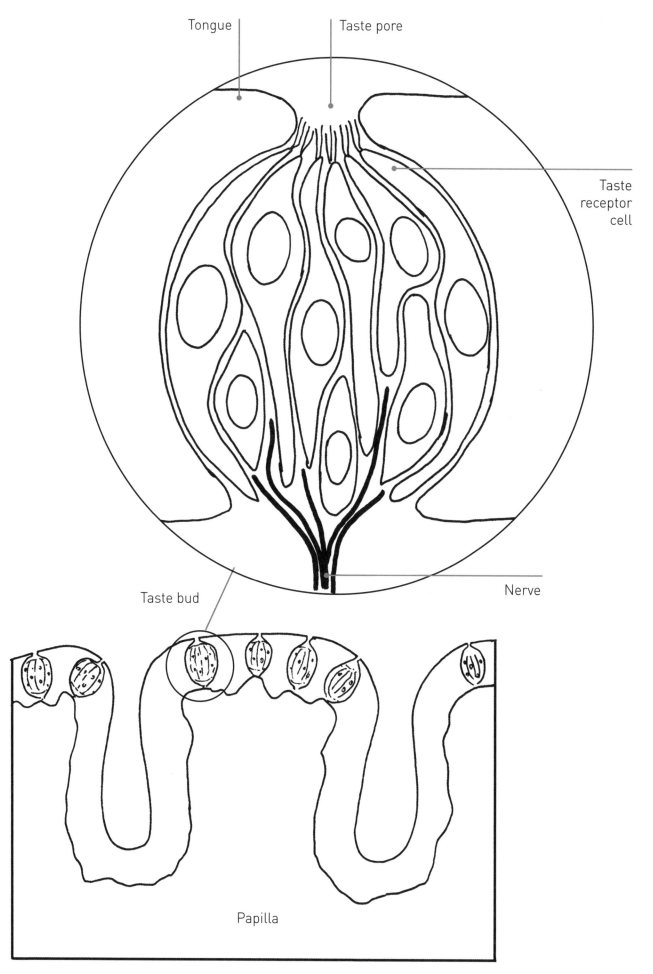

Tongue

Taste pore

Taste receptor cell

Nerve

Taste bud

Papilla

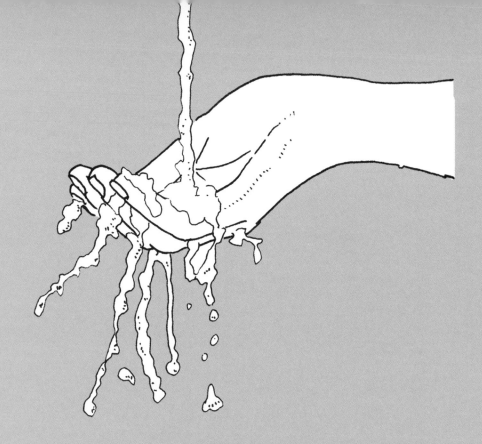

TOUCH

Senses in the skin are measured by tiny receptors at the ends of nerves. There are several different types of receptor. Each type can detect only one kind of sensation, such as pain, temperature, pressure, touch, and so on.

QUICK FACTS

Without this constant flow of information, you would keep **INJURING** yourself accidentally, which is what happens in some rare diseases where the skin senses are lost.

The hands are among the body's most **SENSITIVE** parts.

Skin on the **FINGERTIPS** has the most microsensors, providing the most sensitive touch.

A "**TOUCH TYPIST**" is able to operate computer keys without actually looking at them.

Your sense of touch is more complicated than it seems. It's not just a single sense, detecting physical contact. It's a "multi-sense", detecting:

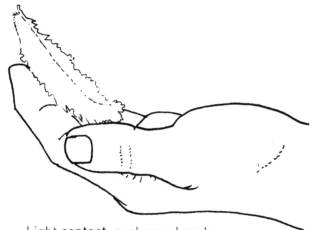

Light **contact**, such as a brush from a feather.

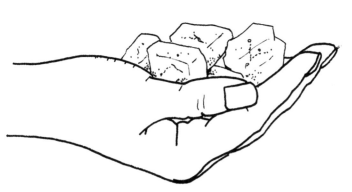

Cold, like an ice cube.

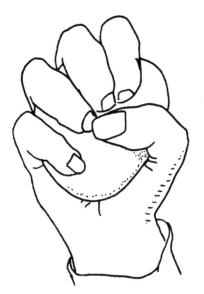

Heavy **pressure**, such as being squeezed hard.

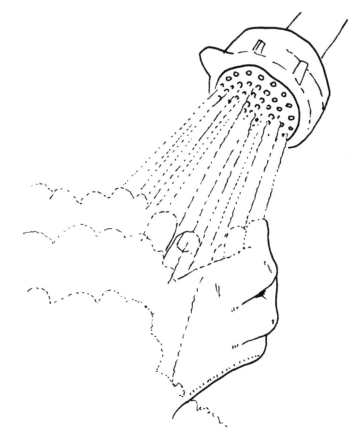

Heat, such as a hot shower or bath.

Movement: your skin can detect movements that are too small for your eye to see.

Surface texture, such as rough wood or smooth plastic.

Moisture content, from dry sand to wet mud.

BONES

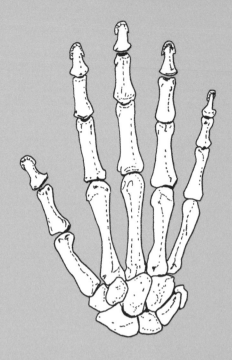

WHAT IS BONE?

A typical bone is actually made of two types of tissue. On the outside is a type of "skin" called the periosteum. Below this is a thin layer of thick, dense, "solid" bone. It is known as hard or compact bony tissue.

Inside this, and forming the bulk of the middle of the bone, is spongy tissue, which has gaps and spaces in it like honeycomb. It is much lighter than the outer compact bone, and the spaces are filled with blood vessels and jelly-like bone marrow for making new blood cells.

QUICK FACTS

More than 99 per cent of the body's **CALCIUM** is contained in the bones and teeth.

Most bones of the skeleton begin in a baby not as real bone, but as a slightly softer, bendier, smooth substance called **CARTILAGE** (gristle).

The nose and ears are mainly cartilage, not true bone, which is why they are slightly **BENDY**.

Even in the **ADULT** skeleton, some bones remain partly cartilage.

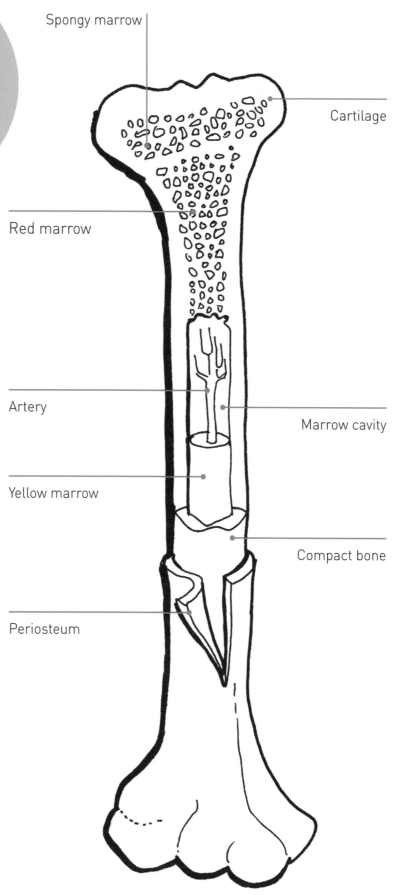

BONE ALSO CONTAINS THREAD-LIKE FIBERS OF COLLAGEN, WHICH MAKE IT SLIGHTLY BENDY UNDER PRESSURE.

Spongy marrow

Cartilage

Red marrow

Artery

Marrow cavity

Yellow marrow

Compact bone

Periosteum

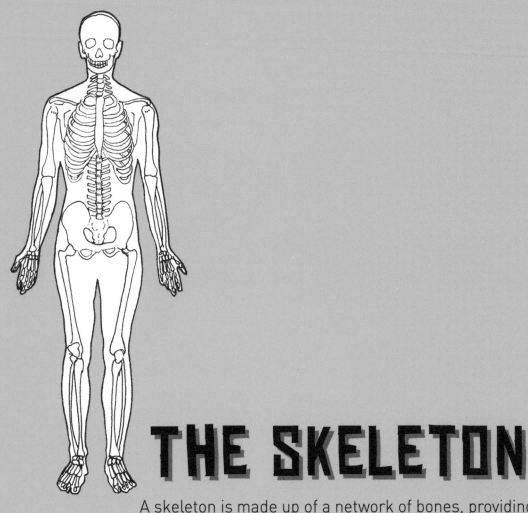

THE SKELETON

A skeleton is made up of a network of bones, providing a frame that holds the whole body together.

Around and under your skeleton is connective tissue, which acts as support, and binds the bones together. It tethers the larger organs to keep them in place, and provides softness for protection.

QUICK FACTS

At **BIRTH**, a baby has 300 bones, but 94 join together in early childhood.

A human skeleton contains, on average, **206** bones.

The skeleton protects delicate **ORGANS** such as the brain, heart, and lungs.

It provides a system of levers that the **MUSCLES** can work on, enabling us to move.

Your **HAND** and **WRIST** alone contain 27 bones.

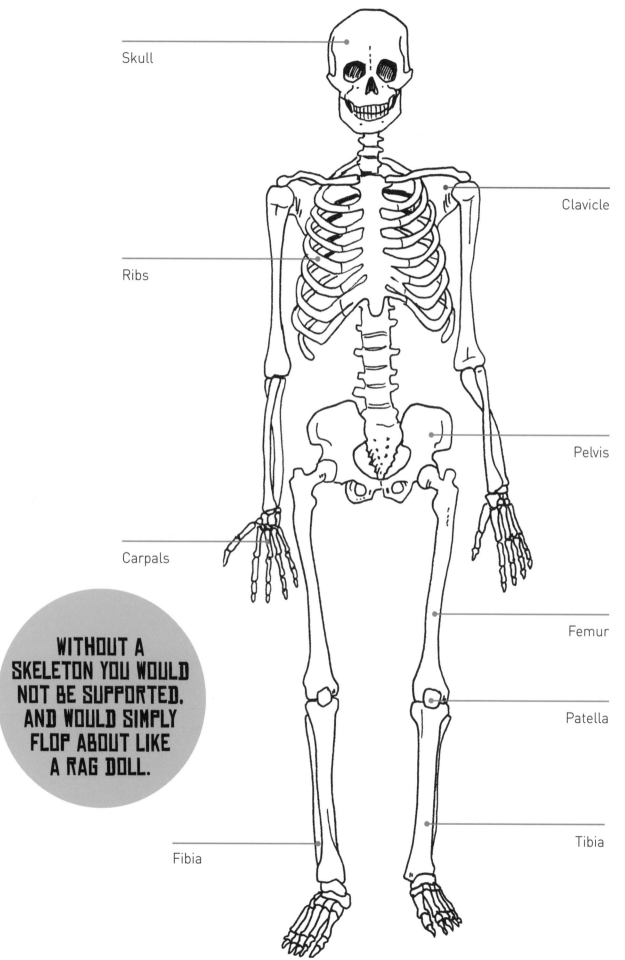

Skull

Clavicle

Ribs

Pelvis

Carpals

WITHOUT A SKELETON YOU WOULD NOT BE SUPPORTED, AND WOULD SIMPLY FLOP ABOUT LIKE A RAG DOLL.

Femur

Patella

Tibia

Fibia

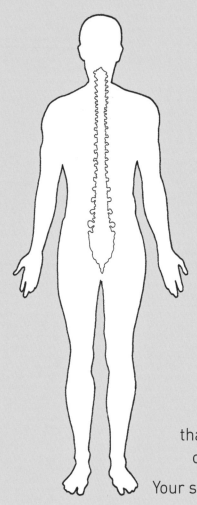

THE SPINE

The spine is the part of the skeleton that extends down the back. It is made up of a column of bones called vertebrae.

Your spine plays an important role in posture and movement, and it also protects your spinal cord.

The vertebrae are held in place by muscles and strong connective tissue called ligaments. Most of the vertebrae have fibrous discs between them to absorb shock and enable the spine to bend.

QUICK FACTS

The spine is also known as the **BACKBONE**.

The human spine consists of 33 **VERTEBRAE**, but some of them grow together in adults.

The spine normally has a slight natural **CURVE**.

Sometimes the intervertebral disc, the tissue that lies between the vertebrae, **STICKS OUT** and presses on nerves.

This condition is called a **SLIPPED DISC**. It can cause severe pain in the lower back, thighs, and legs.

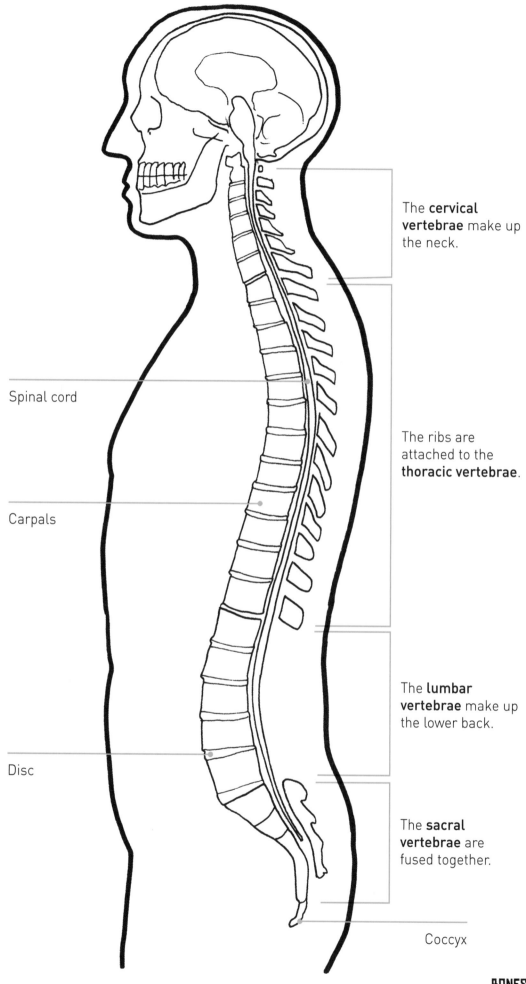

The **cervical vertebrae** make up the neck.

The ribs are attached to the **thoracic vertebrae**.

Spinal cord

Carpals

The **lumbar vertebrae** make up the lower back.

Disc

The **sacral vertebrae** are fused together.

Coccyx

THE JOINTS

A joint is the meeting point between bones, and it usually controls the amount of movement. Some joints have to be strong, while others need to be very mobile.

As it is not possible for joints to be both strong and mobile, we require many different kinds of joints.

QUICK FACTS

Some joints move like a simple **HINGE**, such as those in the shoulder, elbows, and knees. A hinge joint allows extension and flexing.

Others move in **ALL DIRECTIONS**, such as the shoulder joint or the base of the thumb.

Joints in the **SPINE** allow only a small amount of movement.

Your muscles, bones, and joints together are known as the **MUSCULOSKELETAL** system.

Many joints are lubricated with an oily liquid called **SYNOVIAL FLUID** so they can bend freely.

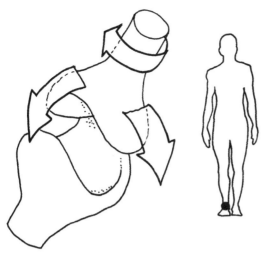

A **saddle** joint allows movement in two directions, but without rotation.

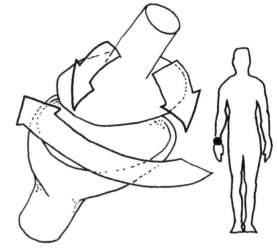

An **ellipsoid** joint allows circular and bending movement, but no rotation.

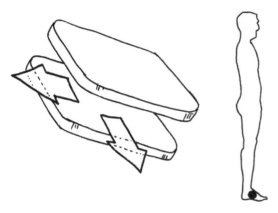

A **plane** joint has a flat surface that allows the bones to slide on each other, but they are restricted.

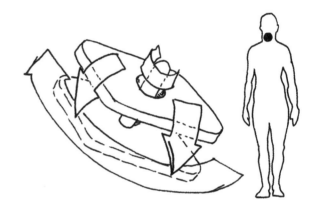

A **pivot** joint allows rotation, but no other movement.

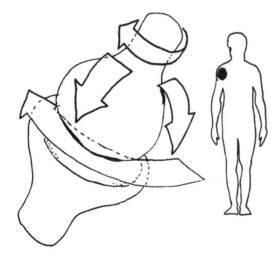

A **ball-and-socket** joint moves freely in all directions.

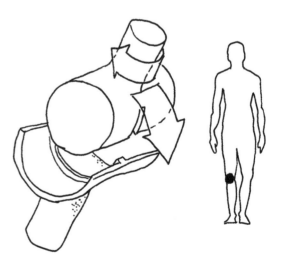

A **hinge** joint allows extension and flexing.

THE MUSCLES

There are 639 muscles in the human body, each comprising around 10 million muscle cells. Each of these cells is like a motor containing 10 cylinders arranged in a row.

The cylinders are tiny boxes that contain fluid, and when a muscle contracts, the brain sends a message to these tiny boxes.

QUICK FACTS

The human body has more than 600 **MAJOR** muscles. About 240 of them have specific names.

Most muscles can be controlled by **CONSCIOUSLY** thinking about them—they move when you want them to.

These are called **VOLUNTARY** muscles, and there are more than 600 of them in your body.

We use 200 voluntary muscles every time we take a **STEP**.

You use about 40 facial muscles to **FROWN**, but only half as many to smile. So save energy by smiling more!

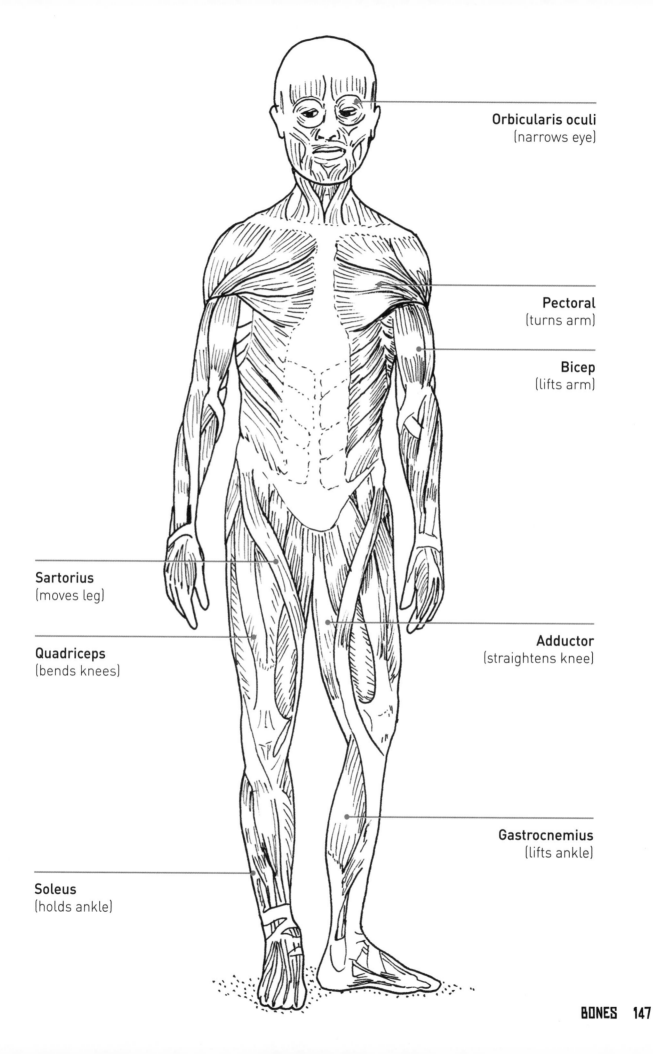

Orbicularis oculi
(narrows eye)

Pectoral
(turns arm)

Bicep
(lifts arm)

Sartorius
(moves leg)

Quadriceps
(bends knees)

Adductor
(straightens knee)

Gastrocnemius
(lifts ankle)

Soleus
(holds ankle)

HOW DO MUSCLES WORK?

Muscles are made up of long, thin cells called muscle fibers.

Muscles work by getting shorter (contracting) and pulling their ends closer together. They can't push, but only pull. They pull against each other most of the time. This keeps them firm, and stops them from becoming floppy.

QUICK FACTS

Your muscles get bigger and **STRONGER** the more you exercise them.

When a muscle contracts, it produces **LACTIC ACID**. This acid is like a poison, with the effect of making the muscle feel tired. If the acid is removed, the muscle stops being tired.

The **LARGEST** muscle in the human body is called the gluteus maximus, and is situated in the buttocks.

The **SMALLEST** is the stapedius, which can be found in the middle ear.

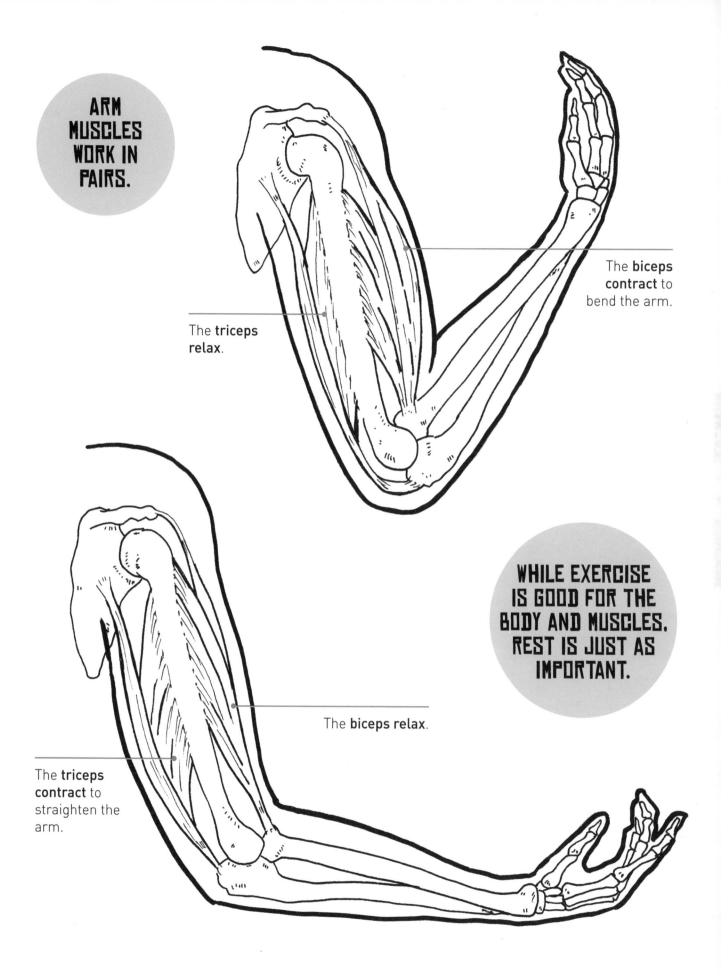

ARM MUSCLES WORK IN PAIRS.

The **biceps contract** to bend the arm.

The **triceps relax**.

WHILE EXERCISE IS GOOD FOR THE BODY AND MUSCLES, REST IS JUST AS IMPORTANT.

The **biceps relax**.

The **triceps contract** to straighten the arm.

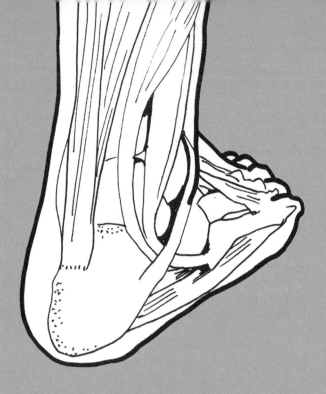

TENDONS

A tendon is a strong white cord that attaches muscles to bones. Muscles move bones by pulling on tendons. Some tendons are round, others are long and flat.

One end of a tendon rises from the end of a muscle, and the other end is woven into the substance of a bone. The tendon may slide up and down inside a sheath of fibrous tissue, in the same way that an arm moves in a coat sleeve.

QUICK FACTS

Tendons are also known as **SINEWS**.

Tendons at the ankle and wrist are enclosed in **SHEATHS** at the points where they cross or are in close contact with other structures.

CONNECTIVE TISSUE is a jelly-like material that binds tendons, muscles, and bones together.

The name "**ACHILLES TENDON**" comes from the legend of Achilles, a Greek hero killed by an arrow in the heel.

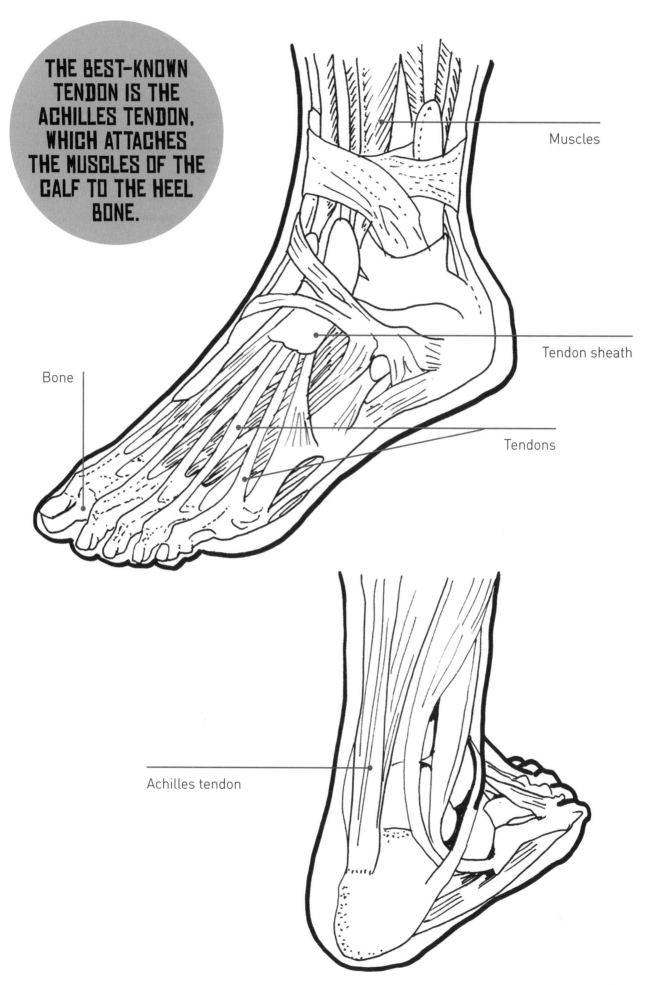

THE BEST-KNOWN TENDON IS THE ACHILLES TENDON, WHICH ATTACHES THE MUSCLES OF THE CALF TO THE HEEL BONE.

Muscles

Tendon sheath

Tendons

Bone

Achilles tendon

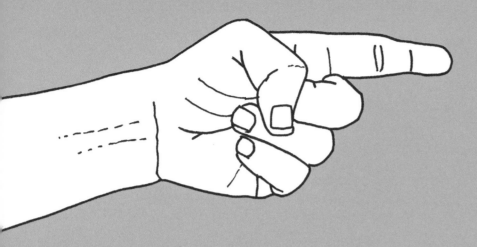

HANDS AND FEET

Your hands and feet have a similar bone structure.

The arrangement of the muscles in your hands and feet gives them great strength without making your fingers and toes so thick that they would be difficult to move.

QUICK FACTS

It takes 35 powerful **MUSCLES** to move the human hand—15 are in the forearm, rather than in the hand itself.

The human **FOOT** has 26 bones.

There are as many as 30 joint surfaces in the human **WRIST** and **HAND**.

The **ELBOW** is the joint that connects a person's upper arm with their forearm.

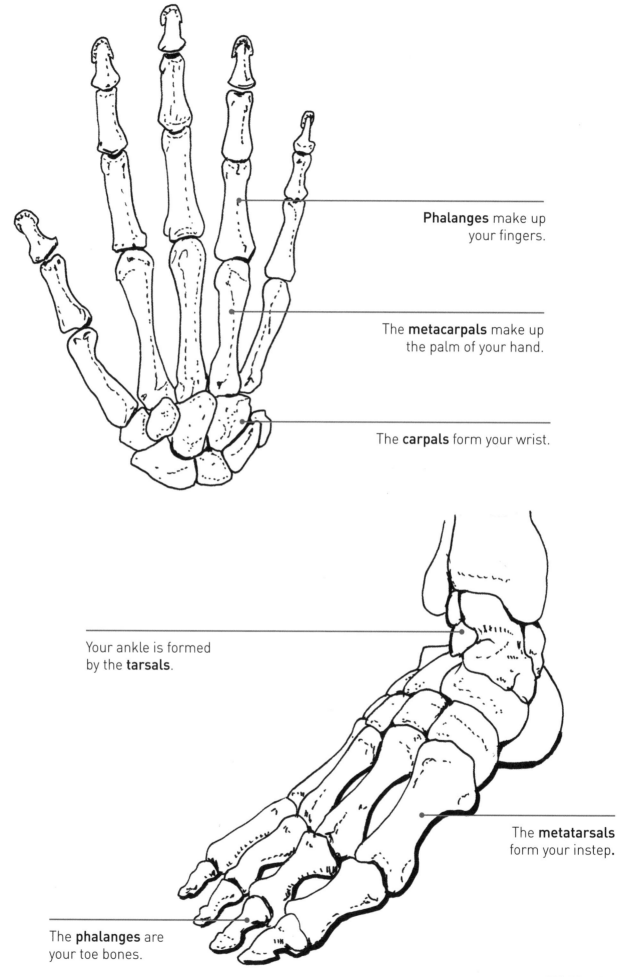

Phalanges make up
your fingers.

The **metacarpals** make up
the palm of your hand.

The **carpals** form your wrist.

Your ankle is formed
by the **tarsals**.

The **metatarsals**
form your instep.

The **phalanges** are
your toe bones.

ARMS AND LEGS

The long bones of the arms and legs work like levers, with their pivot at the joint.

The knee joint is the largest and most complex joint in the body. It moves like a hinge, but it can also rotate and move a little from side to side.

QUICK FACTS

The **HUMERUS** is the body's largest bone. It's also the only bone in the upper arm.

The **PATELLA** (or kneecap) is a small, flat, triangular bone just in front of the joint.

The patella is not directly **CONNECTED** with any other bone. Muscle attachments hold it in place.

The knee **LIGAMENTS** are the strongest connections between the femur and the tibia. They prevent the bones moving out of position.

Soccer requires sturdy knees and ankles.

A **tennis** player must have huge muscular strength in her arms.

THE FLEXIBILITY OF OUR ARMS AND LEGS ALLOWS US TO MAKE THE KIND OF COMPLEX MOVEMENT REQUIRED FOR SPORTS.

A **swimmer** must be strong all over!

REGULATION

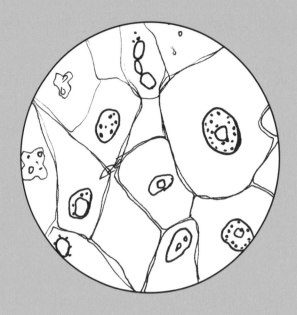

CELLS

Apart from water, the rest of the body is built from a huge number of complicated chemicals. These chemicals, together with water, are assembled into cells.

A cell is the basic unit of life, and all living things are made up of them.

QUICK FACTS

The cell's control area, the **NUCLEUS**, contains all the information and instructions to keep the cell alive and functioning.

The information the cell needs is in the form of long coils of chemicals. These are known as **CHROMOSOMES**.

Cells are able to **DIVIDE** into two very quickly indeed to replace those that are old or have died.

The human body contains more than **50 MILLION MILLION** cells.

The **nucleus** is the focus point of the cell, containing the genetic information as strands of DNA.

The watery, jelly-like **cytoplasm** makes up most of the cell.

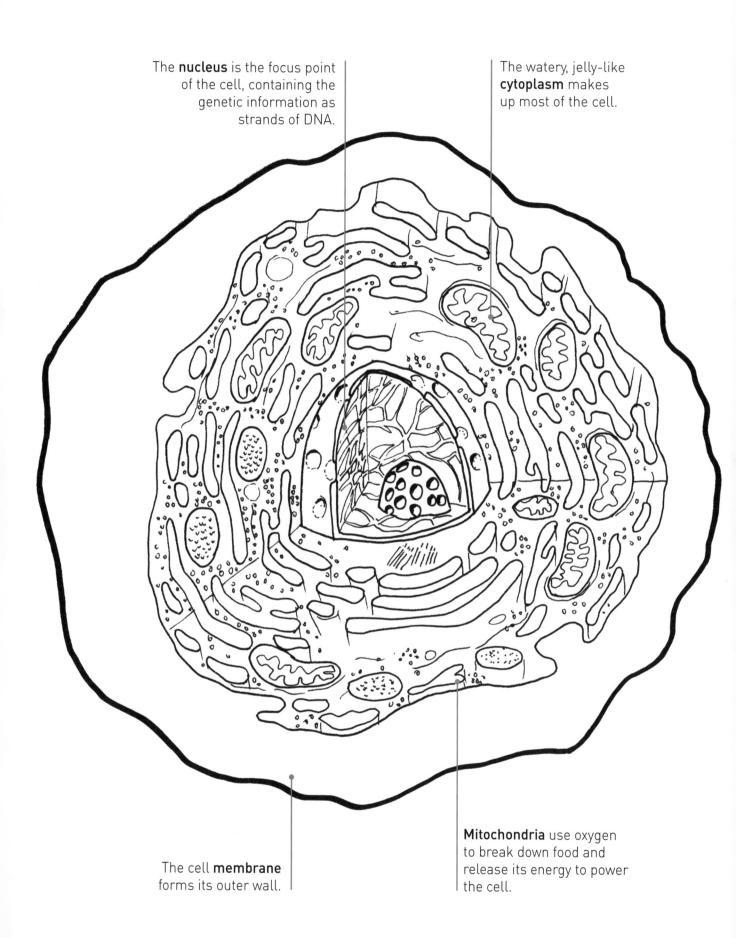

The cell **membrane** forms its outer wall.

Mitochondria use oxygen to break down food and release its energy to power the cell.

TYPES OF CELL

The shape and appearance of a cell depends on what job it does. Each cell is self-contained and has a particular function in the body.

Yet all cells have some things in common. A cell is as alive as you are. It "breathes", takes in food, and gets rid of waste. It also grows and reproduces and, in time, dies.

QUICK FACTS

There are three types of **NERVE** cell, each with a different function.

Most cells are so small they can only be seen with a **MICROSCOPE**.

Some **ONE-CELLED** organisms lead independent lives.

Muscle cells attached to your **EYEBALLS** are moving your eyes across this page!

Skin cells live for 19 days.

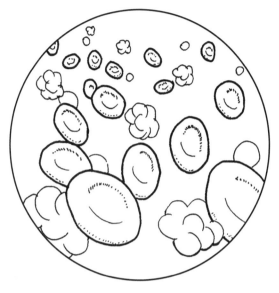

Red **blood** cells live for four months.

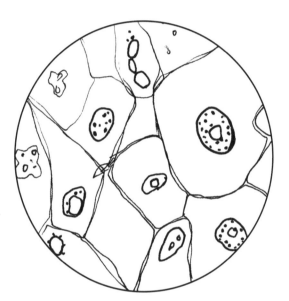

Liver cells live for eight months.

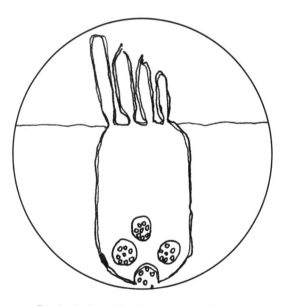

Scalp hair cells live for two–four years.

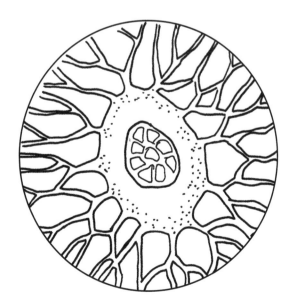

Bone cells live for 15–25 years.

MAINTAINING CELLS

Cells need food, oxygen, and a watery environment in order to survive. Food and water are supplied by the blood and other body fluids, which also carry away waste.

Blood contains all of the food substances and chemicals needed by the cell.

QUICK FACTS

All cells have a fixed **LIFESPAN** and are replaced automatically as they die off.

Cells lining the **INTESTINE** live for about five days before being replaced.

Other nerve cells within the **BRAIN** can survive throughout your entire life.

Nerve cells are the only ones that cannot be **REPLACED**, but even nerve cells can sometimes grow new connections if the message paths become damaged.

The cells in children and young adults are able to repair themselves when **DAMAGED**.

This is not the case in older people, where the process is not as **EFFICIENT**.

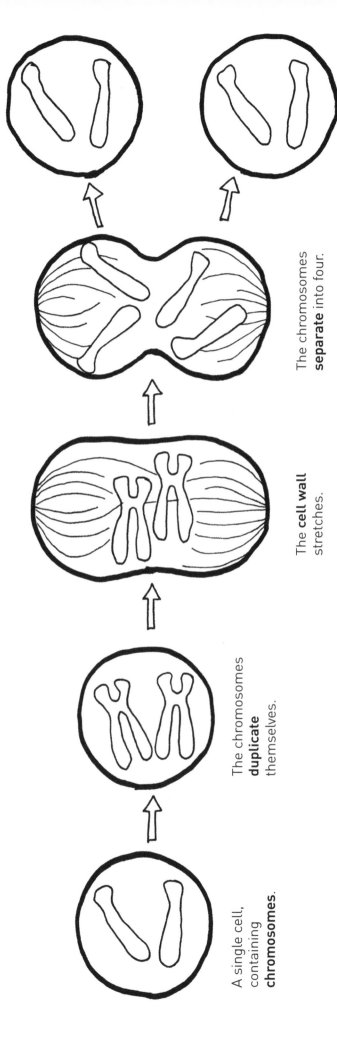

Now there are **two** separate cells.

The chromosomes **separate** into four.

The **cell wall** stretches.

The chromosomes **duplicate** themselves.

A single cell, containing **chromosomes.**

MITOSIS IS **THE PROCESS OF A CELL DIVIDING ITSELF INTO TWO.**

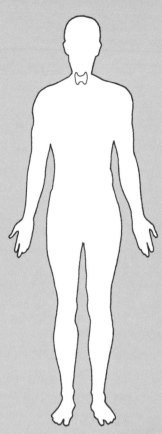

THE METABOLISM

Our metabolism is the sum of all chemical activity in our cells which break down the food we take in.

Our metabolic rate increases with vigorous exercise, which means that we use the energy produced by food much more efficiently.

QUICK FACTS

The body's need for energy from the diet **VARIES** not only with activity, sex, health, and climate, but also with age.

Up to two years old, a rapidly growing **CHILD** needs more than anyone in proportion to its own size.

By **OLD AGE**, when metabolism is slowest, the need is far less.

The **THYROID** is a bow-tie-shaped gland under the kink of the neck. Its hormones accelerate the release of energy from food and help control our metabolism.

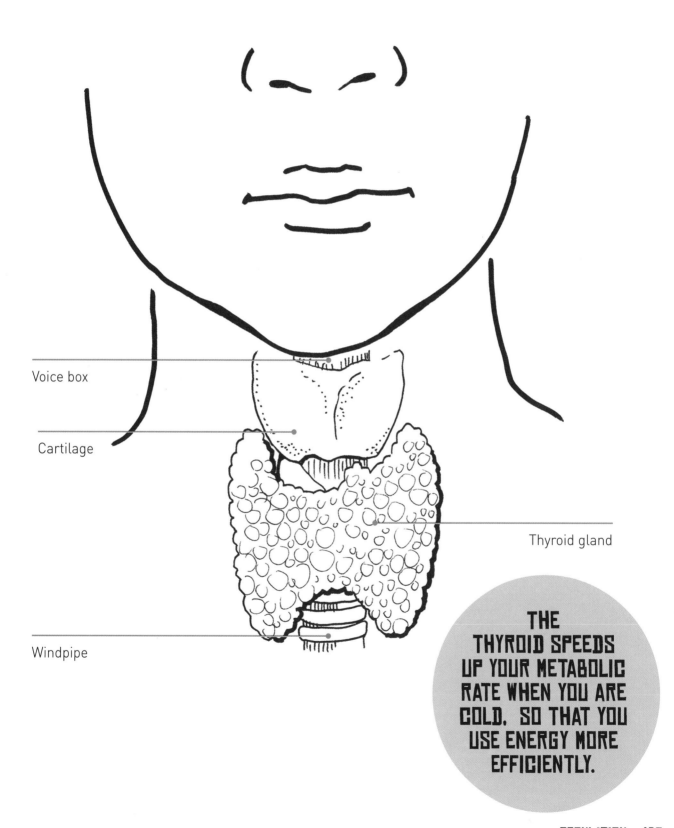

Voice box

Cartilage

Windpipe

Thyroid gland

THE THYROID SPEEDS UP YOUR METABOLIC RATE WHEN YOU ARE COLD, SO THAT YOU USE ENERGY MORE EFFICIENTLY.

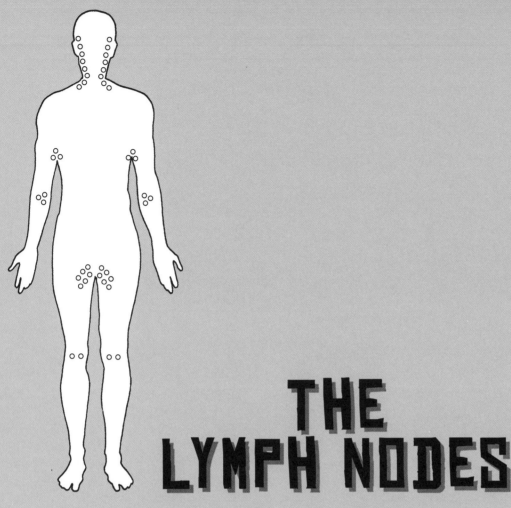

THE LYMPH NODES

Your body's main attack force is called the lymph system.
Like the blood system, it is a set of vessels that
carry liquid around the body.

This liquid is called lymph. It contains special white blood cells
called lymphocytes, which fight germs and cope with poisons.

QUICK FACTS

There are about 500 lymph **NODES** all over the body.

Lymph nodes and **VESSELS** are found in most body
parts, especially in the neck, armpits, chest, central
abdomen, and groin.

Lymph nodes are mostly **SHAPED** like balls, beans,
or pears.

The **SMALLEST** ones are 6–8 in. across.

Your lymph nodes can double in size when **FIGHTING** illness.

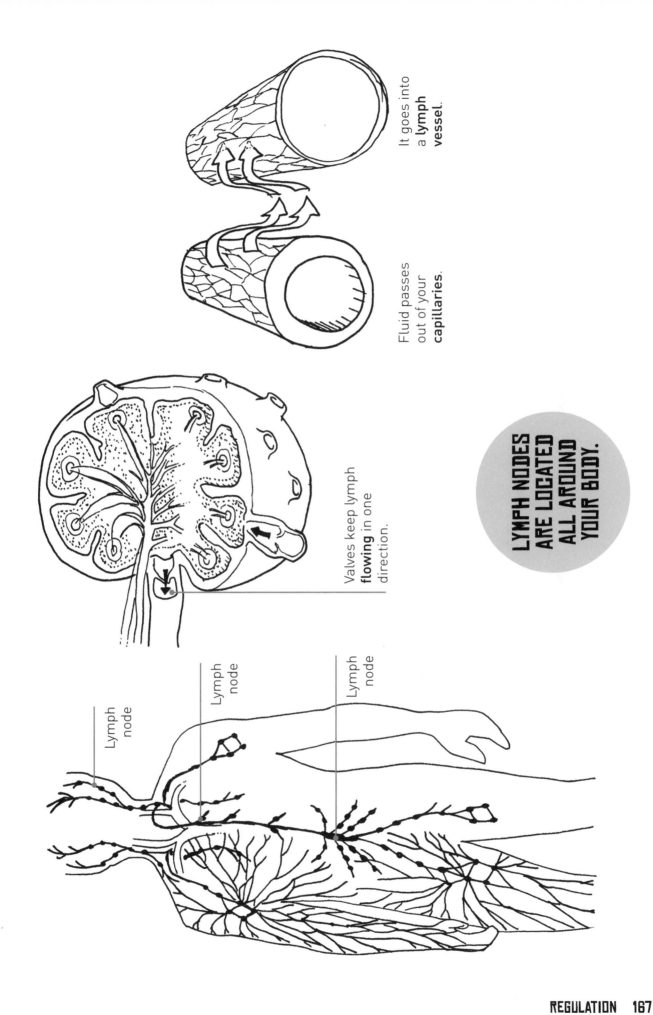

It goes into a **lymph vessel.**

Fluid passes out of your **capillaries.**

Valves keep lymph **flowing** in one direction.

LYMPH NODES ARE LOCATED ALL AROUND YOUR BODY.

Lymph node

Lymph node

Lymph node

THE IMMUNE SYSTEM

As we grow up, our bodies naturally develop immunity to most diseases. There are only a few we need to be protected from artificially, through immunizations.

Once we have caught an illness and fought the infection, we have immunity to the germ in the future.

QUICK FACTS

The immune system also helps to clean away **DEBRIS** from normal body maintenance as old cells die.

After the body catches an infection, especially a virus, white cells called memory cells "**REMEMBER**" the type of virus.

If the germ invades again later, the immune system can recognize and fight against it straightaway and usually defeat it quickly. This is called being **RESISTANT**, or immune, to that particular germ.

A bad night's **SLEEP** can affect your immune system. It can reduce the number of natural killer cells in your body, so weakening your disease-fighting abilities.

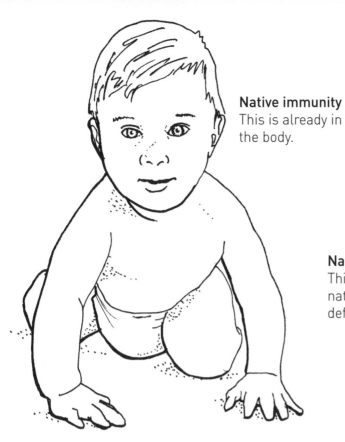

Native immunity
This is already in the body.

Natural acquired immunity
This happens when the body naturally catches and defeats the germ.

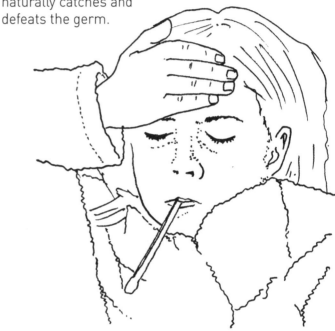

Acquired immunity
This occurs after exposure to antigens, for example, on the surface of a type of germ.

Artificial acquired immunity
An altered form of the germ or its products is put into the body specially, by vaccination.

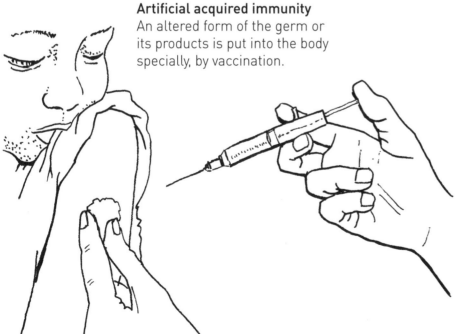

Passive immunity
Ready-made antibodies are put into the body.

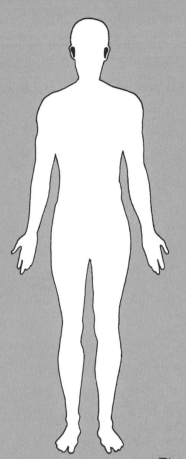

BALANCE

The inner ear is the body's main organ of balance.

The brain also receives messages from the nerve endings in the neck, back, leg, and feet muscles. It sifts all this information and sends messages to the muscles, allowing us to perform incredible feats of balance, such as ice-skating.

QUICK FACTS

The **EYES** supply information about what is upright and level.

The skin, muscles, and joints report whether the body is **LEANING**.

You feel **DIZZY** after you spin round and round because the liquid in your ears is still swirling about when you stop, and your brain can't tell where you're going!

In space, there is no gravity to help to give astronauts a sense of balance. The lack of gravity causes about a third of people to get **SPACE SICK**.

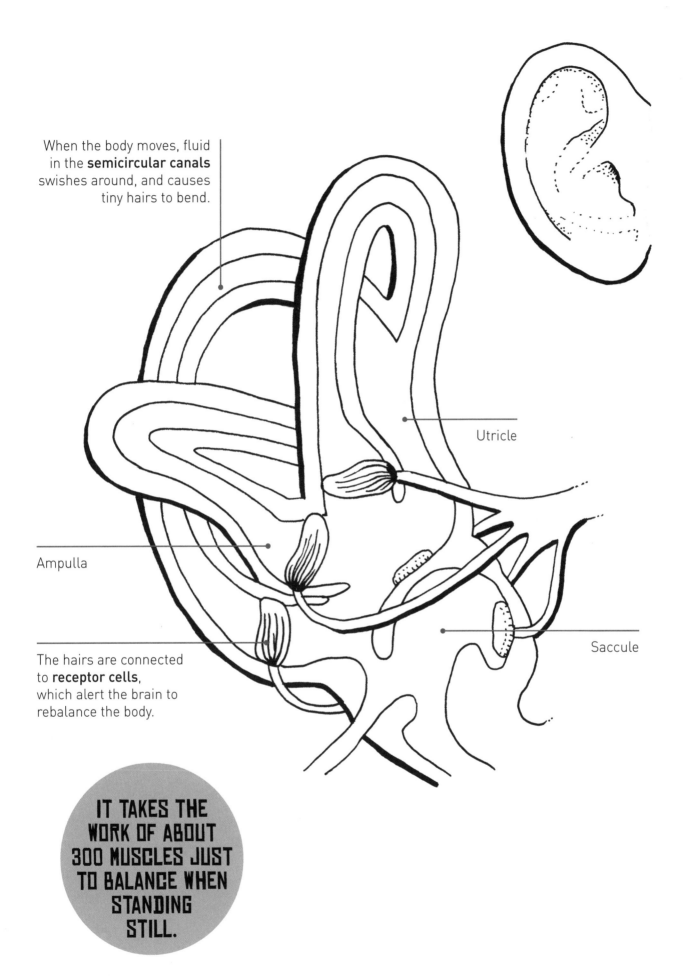

When the body moves, fluid in the **semicircular canals** swishes around, and causes tiny hairs to bend.

Utricle

Ampulla

Saccule

The hairs are connected to **receptor cells**, which alert the brain to rebalance the body.

IT TAKES THE WORK OF ABOUT 300 MUSCLES JUST TO BALANCE WHEN STANDING STILL.

BODY TEMPERATURE

Your body needs energy to keep going. There are substances in the body whose job it is to combine oxygen with fuel (the food you eat) in an orderly, controlled way in order to supply this energy.

The body maintains an average level of heat regardless of what is going on outside. This is done by the brain's temperature center.

The name for the regulation of your body's temperature is homeostasis.

QUICK FACTS

Body movements can be homeostatic. A person feeling **COLD** curls up.

A person feeling too **HOT** may spread out their arms and legs.

SHIVERING produces heat. It is our body's automatic reaction to our blood temperature dropping too low.

Humans have a **NORMAL** body temperature of 98.6°F.

Curling up reduces the area of the body losing warmth.

Spreading out your arms and legs increases **heat loss**.

Shivering makes you **warmer**, just as running or other physical movement does.

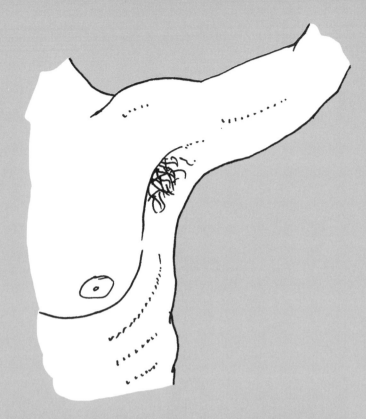

PERSPIRATION

Perspiration (sweating) is one of the ways that the body is kept at a normal temperature.

The fluid flows out through millions of tiny openings (pores) in the skin, in the form of microscopic drops.

QUICK FACTS

Perspiration works because when a liquid **EVAPORATES** it takes heat from wherever it is located.

It is like a **SHOWER** that washes the body out from within.

Your skin goes red when you are hot because of the increased flow of **BLOOD** in vessels near your skin.

An adult human has more than two million sweat **GLANDS** in their body. The highest concentration of these is in the feet!

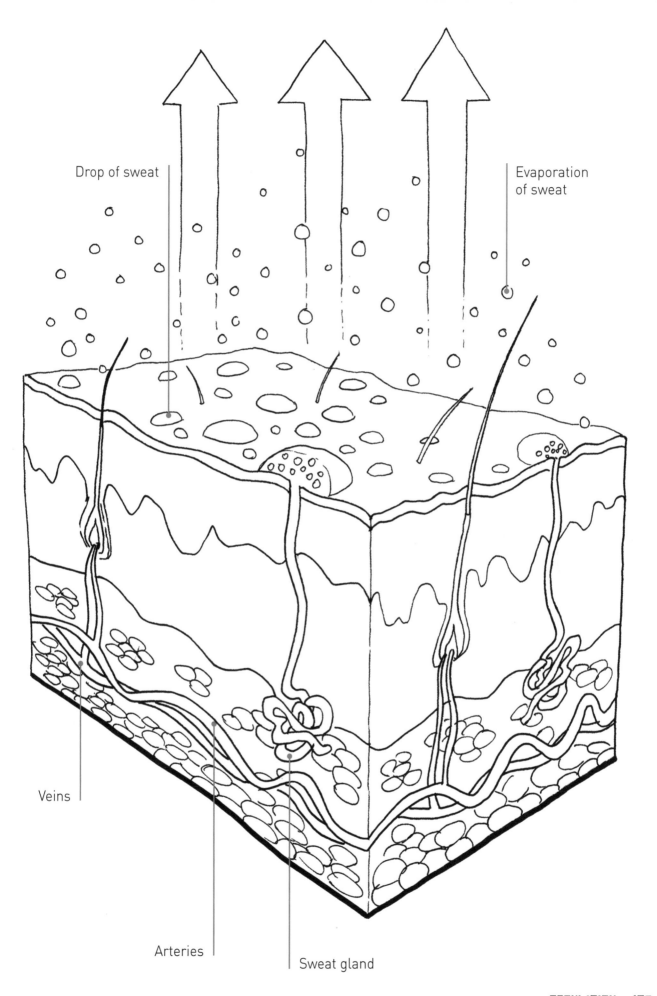

Drop of sweat

Evaporation
of sweat

Veins

Arteries

Sweat gland

GROWING

People's bodies grow faster in the early weeks of life than at any other time. Through the whole period of childhood, they grow at a moderate rate. Then growth starts to speed up again.

We continue to grow, but only slightly, after the age of 25, and we reach our maximum height at about the age of 35 or 40.

QUICK FACTS

The **TALLEST** person ever measured was 8 ft 11 in. tall.

Growth is controlled by the **ENDOCRINE** glands.

After the age of 40, we **SHRINK** about half an inch every 10 years. This is because cartilage in our joints and in the spinal column dries up as we get older.

Older people are no longer growing, and are often not as active as they used to be. For these reasons they do not need to eat as much and often become **THINNER**.

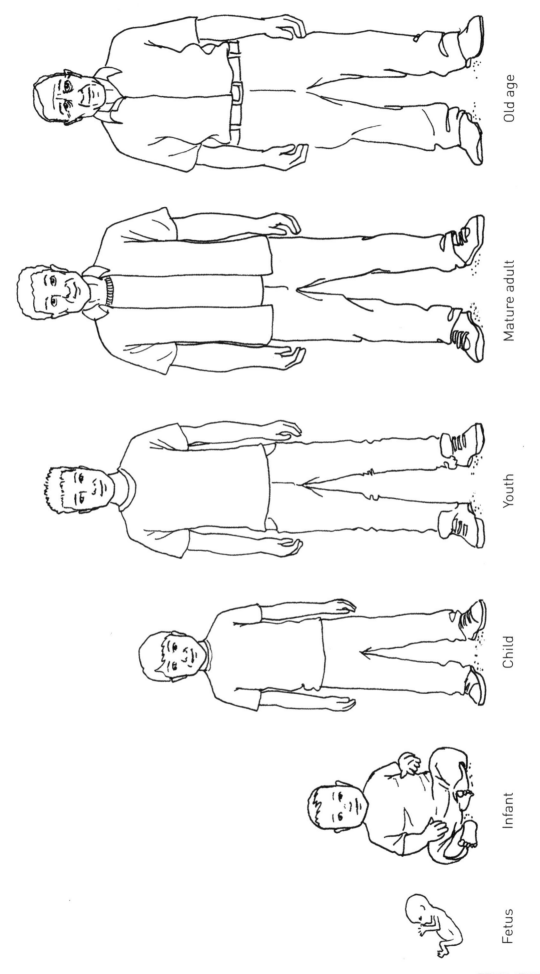

Old age

Mature adult

Youth

Child

Infant

Fetus

AGING

Aging is a result of the gradual failure of the body's cells and organs to replace and repair themselves. This is because there is a limit to the number of times that each cell can divide.

Sometimes the new cells that are produced have defects or do not carry out their usual task effectively. Organs can then begin to fail, tissues change in structure, and the chemical reactions that power the body become less efficient.

QUICK FACTS

The world **POPULATION** is getting older. Some estimates suggest that there will be 395 million people in the world aged 80 or over by 2050.

Strangely, even though recent events may be forgotten, old people often clearly remember events that took place in their **CHILDHOOD**.

The **SKIN** becomes looser as people age. As skin sags, it forms into wrinkles and creases because the fibers of collagen that normally provide support to the skin become weaker.

The first **SENSE** to deteriorate is usually hearing, followed by sight.

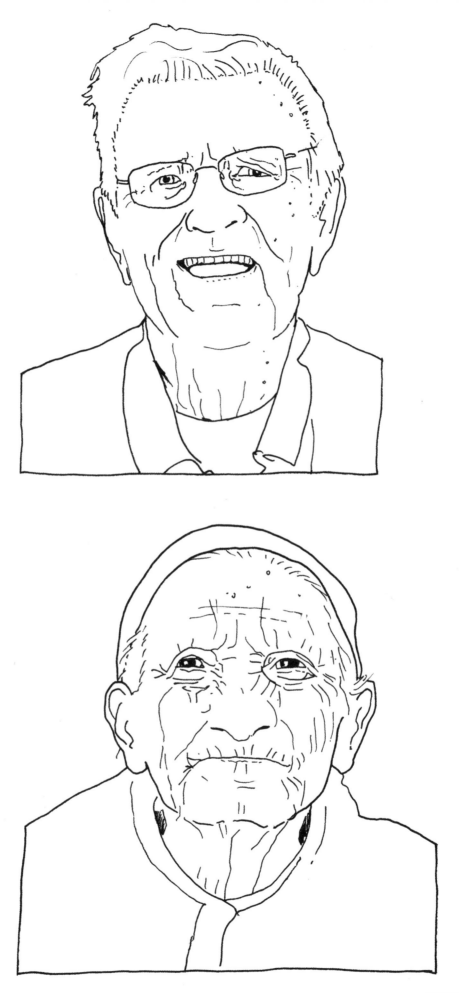

EXERCISE

Regular exercise is important because it keeps bones, joints, and muscles healthy.

During any physical exertion, the rate at which the heart beats increases, as it pumps more oxygenated blood around the body. How quickly their heart rate returns to normal after exercise is one way to assess how fit someone is, and how exercise is actually improving their fitness.

QUICK FACTS

SWIMMING is a very good form of exercise as it uses lots of muscles without causing strain.

There was a time when almost everyone did **MANUAL** work of some kind. It was essential for survival.

Human bodies were not designed for the **INACTIVE** lives many of us now lead. That is why exercise is important for good health.

Exercise can help you do better at school. Cardiovascular exercise helps to create new brain cells, and in return this increases your **BRAINPOWER**.

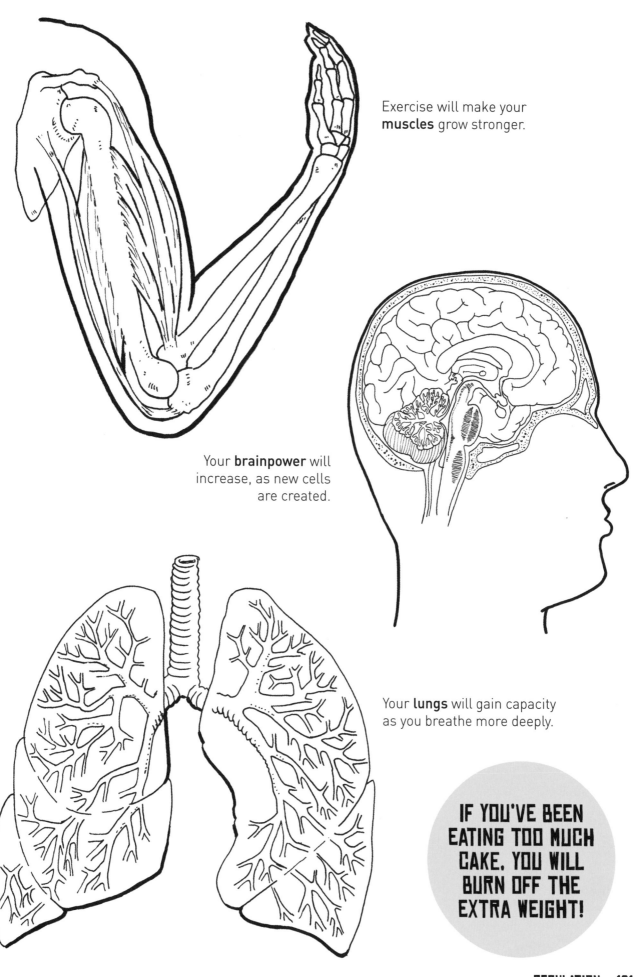

Exercise will make your **muscles** grow stronger.

Your **brainpower** will increase, as new cells are created.

Your **lungs** will gain capacity as you breathe more deeply.

IF YOU'VE BEEN EATING TOO MUCH CAKE, YOU WILL BURN OFF THE EXTRA WEIGHT!

ON THE OUTSIDE

HAIR

Hairs are glued-together rods of dead, flattened, microscopic cells filled with a tough, hard substance called keratin.

A hair grows at its root, which is buried in a pocket in the skin called a follicle. Skin feels smooth, but under a microscope it looks like a jagged mountain range with huge pits of sprouting hair.

QUICK FACTS

A single hair has a **LIFESPAN** of about five years.

As soon as a hair is **PLUCKED** from a follicle, a new one starts to grow.

The human body has hairs **ALL OVER**, apart from a few places such as the palms, the sides of the fingers, and the soles of the feet.

At night, head hair **GROWS** slowly, but as day begins, this is speeded up.

Between 10 and 11am, the **SPEED** of growth is at its greatest. Then the hair grows slowly again.

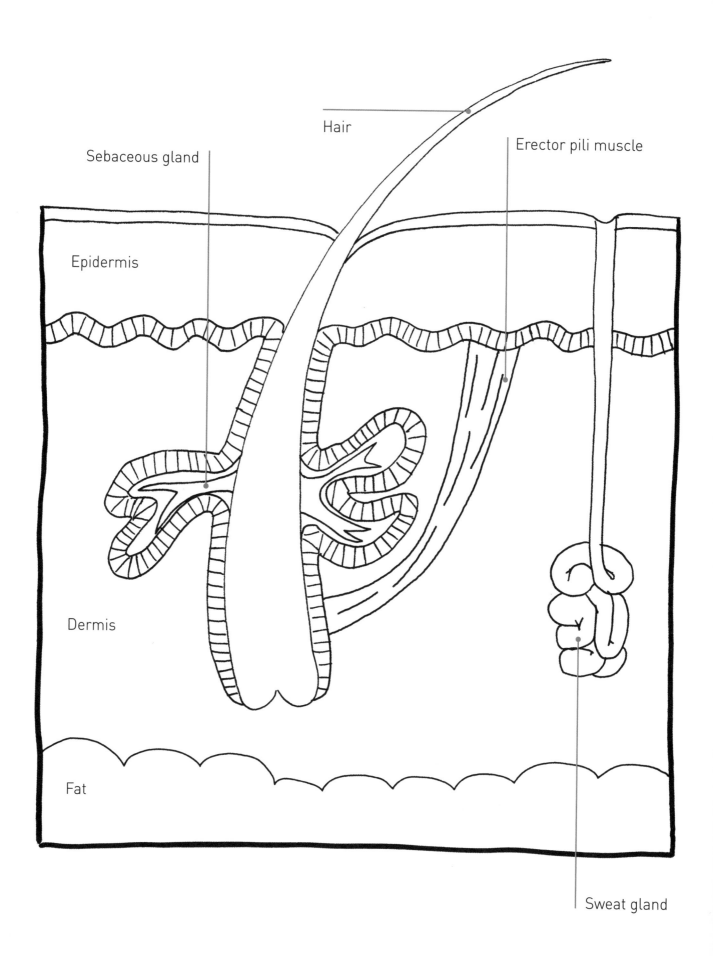

Hair

Erector pili muscle

Sebaceous gland

Epidermis

Dermis

Fat

Sweat gland

HEAD HAIR

The number of hairs you have on your head depends on your hair color. Most blonds have about 140,000 head hairs, and redheads average 90,000, while people with black or brown hair come somewhere in the middle with about 110,000 hairs.

QUICK FACTS

Most follicles contain an oil gland called the **SEBACEOUS** gland. This secretes oil into the follicle. The oil flows over the hair, lubricating it and keeping it soft.

Most kinds of hairs **GROW** for a time, gradually slow down, then "rest" and hardly grow at all.

Most people's hair gradually becomes gray or white as they grow older, because melanin, the **PIGMENT** that gives hair its color, no longer forms.

Hair is **straight** or **curly** depending on the shape of the follicle from which it grows.

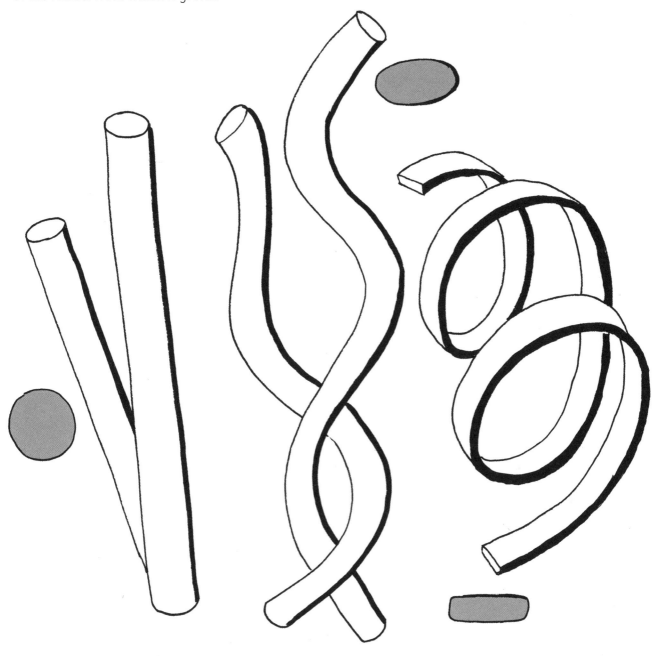

Straight hair grows from completely round follicles.

Wavy hair comes from oval follicles.

Very **curly** hair grows from flattened follicles.

FAIR OR BLOND HAIRS ARE USUALLY THINNER THAN DARK OR BLACK HAIRS.

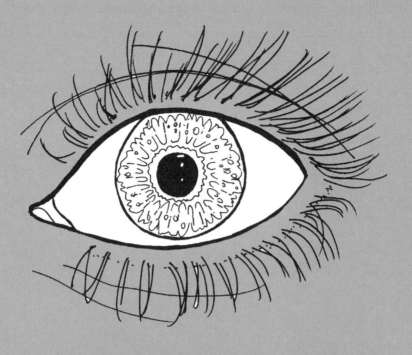

EYEBROWS AND EYELASHES

Eyebrows and eyelashes perform useful functions.
Eyebrow hairs stop sweat dripping into your eyes. Eyelash hairs help
to whisk away bits of wind-blown dust, dirt, and pests such as insects.

QUICK FACTS

Eyelashes are the **THICKEST** hairs you have. They are up
to 0.03 in. thick.

Eyebrow hairs have a **LIFE CYCLE** of about 20 weeks.
During that time they all fall out and new ones grow.

For eyelashes, the **CYCLE** lasts around 10 weeks.

Eyebrow hairs grow only a tiny 0.006 in. per day, usually
reaching 0.4 in. at maximum **LENGTH**.

Eyelash hairs grow at a similar **RATE**, but usually stop
growing at 0.3 in. long.

Eyebrows and eyelashes grow in **different patterns** on different people.
Add them to all these eyes.

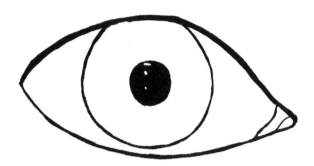
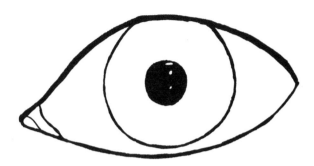
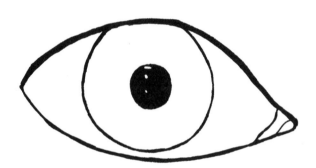
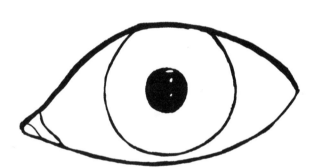
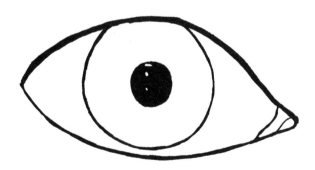
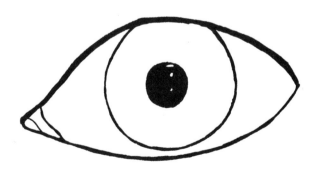

BODY HAIR

Babies are born covered with fine down, which is soon replaced by delicate hair. At puberty, this transforms into the final coat of hair which the person will have as an adult.

The development of adult hair is regulated by the glands. Male hormones work in such a way that the beard and body hair are developed, while the growth of the hair on the head is slowed down. The action of female hormones is exactly the opposite.

QUICK FACTS

Body hairs **STAND ON END** when you're cold. Each one is pulled by the erector pili, a tiny muscle attached to its root.

This hair-raising "**BLANKET**" around the body helps to trap air and so keeps in body warmth.

Our hair can also stand on end when we are **FRIGHTENED**.

As we grow up, hairs also appear under our arms (**AXILLARY** hair) and between our legs (**PUBIC** hair).

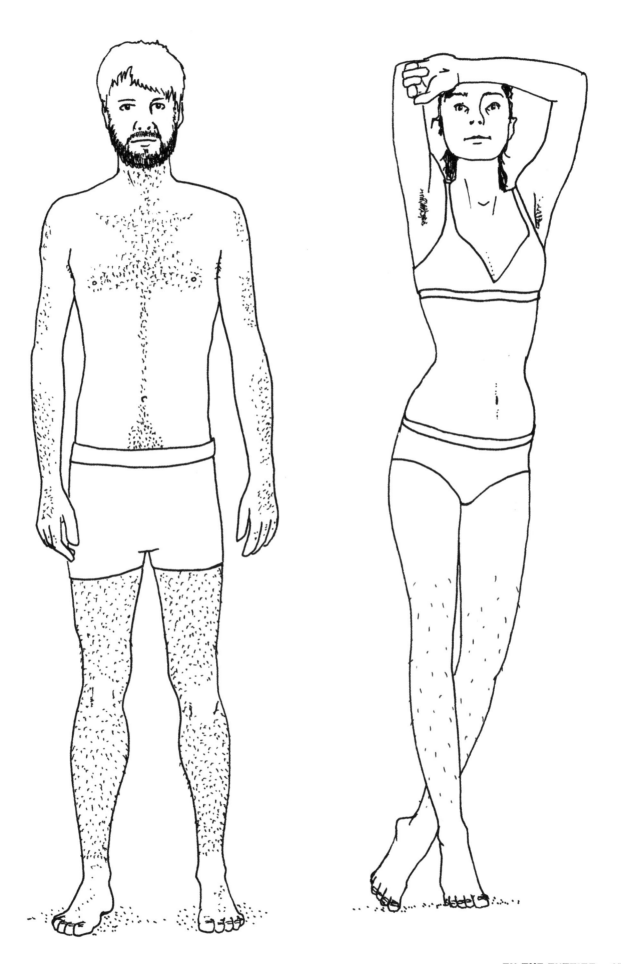

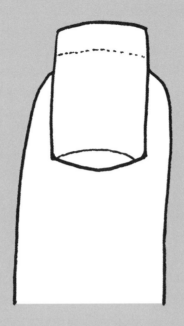

NAILS

A nail is a strong, stiff, flat plate made of keratin, the same dead substance as hairs. Each nail acts as a rigid pad on the back of the finger. Without the nail, the whole fingertip would bend back.

QUICK FACTS

When you press gently on an object, the fingertip is **SQUEEZED** between it and the nail. This makes it easier to judge pressure and the hardness of the object.

Most nails **GROW** about 0.01 in. each week.

In general, **FINGERNAILS** grow faster than toenails. Nails grow faster in summer than in winter.

If you are **RIGHT-HANDED**, the nails on your right hand grow faster than those on your left. It is the other way around if you are left-handed.

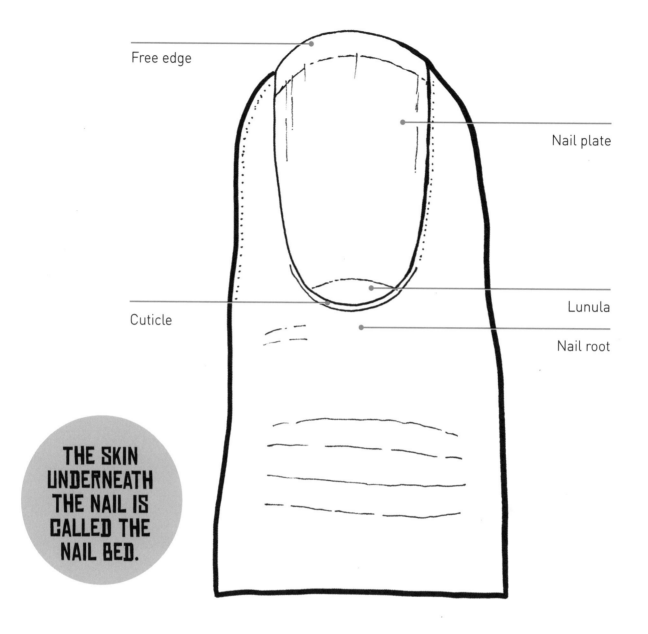

Free edge

Nail plate

Cuticle

Lunula

Nail root

THE SKIN UNDERNEATH THE NAIL IS CALLED THE NAIL BED.

Fingernails come in three different basic **shapes**.

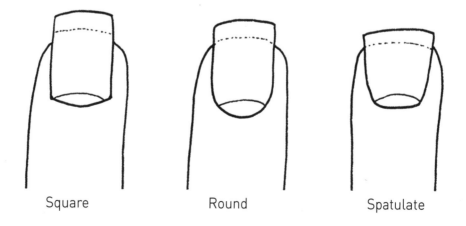

Square

Round

Spatulate

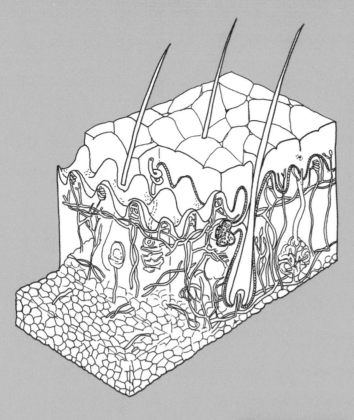

SKIN

Skin is a flexible, waterproof covering that protects us from the outside world. It prevents harmful germs from entering the body.

Your skin is your largest organ and it is sensitive to touch, temperature, and pain. It tells you what is happening around your body, so you can avoid injuring yourself, and also helps to prevent damage from the Sun's harmful ultraviolet rays.

QUICK FACTS

Every minute, your skin **SHEDS** 30,000 dead cells.

A large amount of the **DUST** in your house is actually dead skin.

Skin makes itself **THICKER** where it is worn or rubbed.

It **WEARS AWAY** every month, but it replaces itself every month, too.

The **WEIGHT** of the skin is about 7 lbs for a typical adult, twice as heavy as the next-largest organ, the liver.

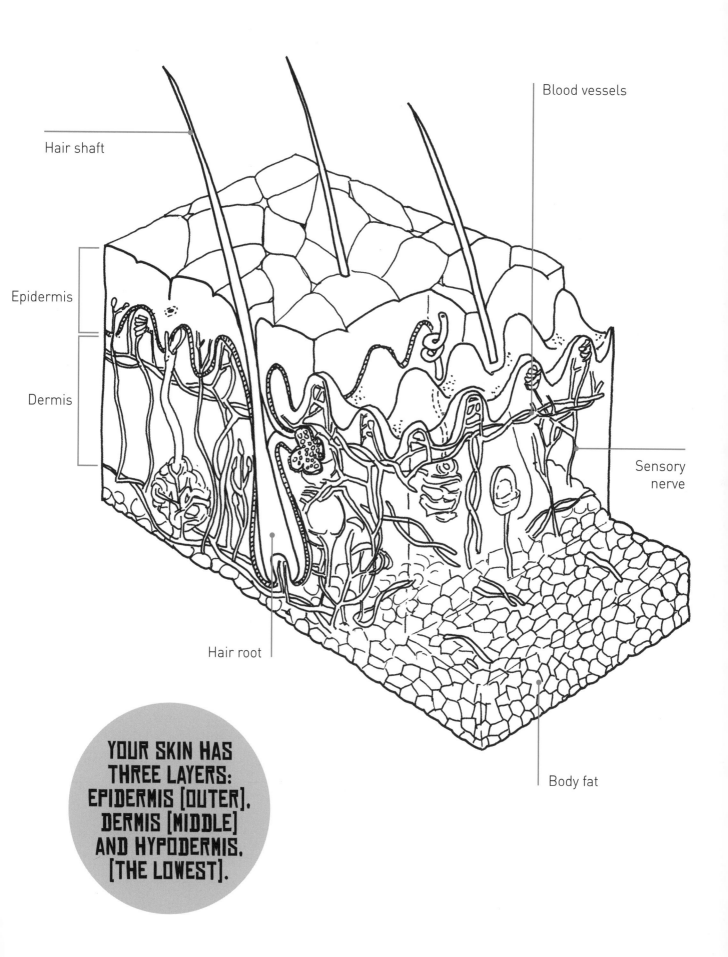

Hair shaft

Blood vessels

Epidermis

Dermis

Sensory nerve

Hair root

Body fat

YOUR SKIN HAS THREE LAYERS: EPIDERMIS [OUTER], DERMIS [MIDDLE] AND HYPODERMIS, [THE LOWEST].

SKIN COLOR

All the colors of the human race arise from different combinations of certain ingredients we all have in our skin. The base color of skin is creamy white, and a yellow pigment is present, too. Skin also contains tiny granules of a substance called melanin. Although they are brown in color, when there are a lot of them, they appear to be black.

QUICK FACTS

A further **TONE** is added to the skin by the tinge of red blood circulating in tiny blood vessels.

Skin develops extra melanin when it is exposed to strong sunlight. Tiny grains are produced in the skin cells and spread to produce an even **SUNTAN**.

Suntan helps protect against **DAMAGE**.

Over time, the appearance of skin changes: it becomes more **WRINKLED** and creased. As people age, their skin becomes looser.

Pigments are natural colorings found in everyone's skin.

Carotene pigments give the skin a yellowish appearance, which is commonly found in people with Chinese ancestry.

Everyone has different amounts of **melanin** in their skin. **Pheomelanin** produces pale skin.

Eumelanin protects against the sun's radiation. People whose ancestors lived in Africa have a lot of eumelanin, which gives them dark-brown or black skin.

The Indian subcontinent is a warm place, but cooler than Africa. People whose ancestors lived there have a medium amount of **eumelanin**, giving them mid-brown skin.

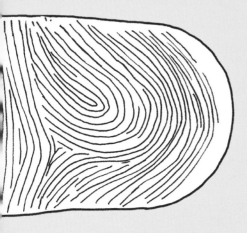

FINGERPRINTS

If you look very closely at a fingerprint, you will notice that it is made up of ridges on the skin. These ridges aren't always continuous; they stop, split into two, form little pockets (called "lakes"), and even appear to cross each other at times.

It is these individual features that make the difference between one fingerprint and the next.

QUICK FACTS

The loops and spirals on your fingertips help you to **GRIP** things when picking them up.

Fingerprints are formed before **BIRTH**, during the development of the hands.

Fingerprints are not actually formed in the skin, but are caused by **RIDGES** in the flesh underneath the skin.

Fingerprints fall into a set number of general **PATTERNS**, which allows us to catalog them and perform fingerprint searches more easily.

UP CLOSE, FINGERPRINTS ARE AMAZINGLY INTRICATE—AND THEY ARE ALL DIFFERENT. TRY TO DRAW YOUR OWN!

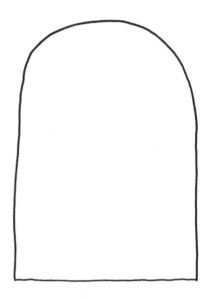

HEALTH

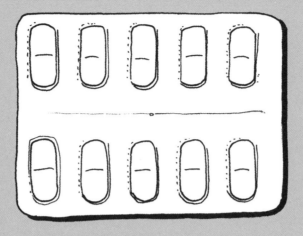

DISEASES AND MEDICINE

A disease or illness stops your body working normally. Medicine involves finding out how diseases can be cured or prevented, and modern medical technologies allow doctors to diagnose and treat many illnesses.

QUICK FACTS

Most people are healthy most of the time, but a few seem to be unlucky and get **ILL** quite often.

To keep your body **HEALTHY**, eat a nutritous diet, take plenty of exercise, and keep a positive attitude to life.

It can be quite difficult for young **CHILDREN** to describe their symptoms. This can make diagnosis tricky.

HIGH-TECH methods such as CT scans allow doctors to look inside a living body for possible problems.

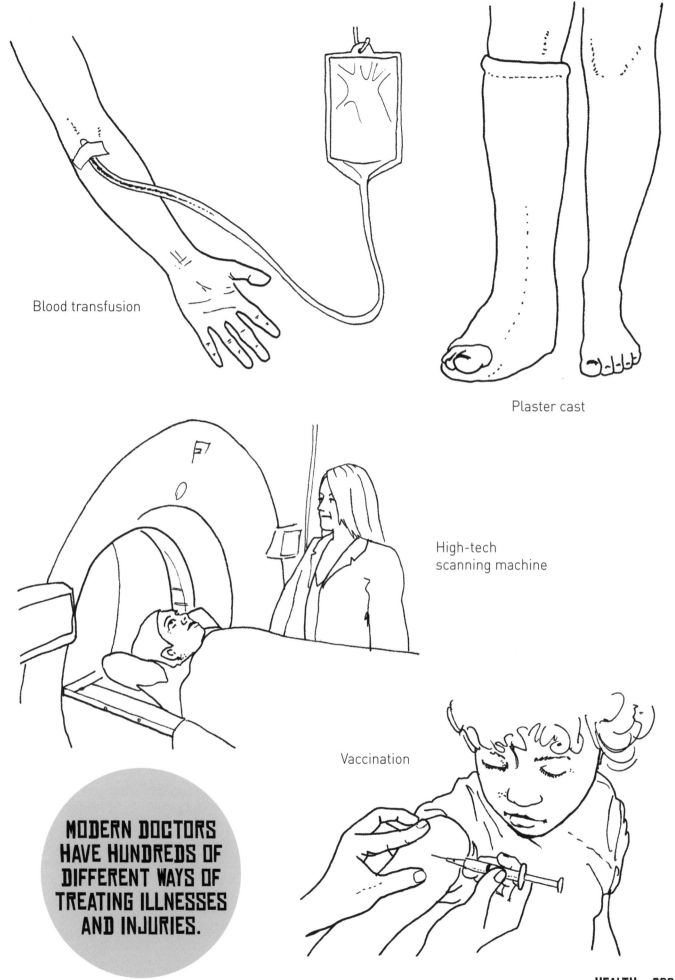

Blood transfusion

Plaster cast

High-tech
scanning machine

Vaccination

MODERN DOCTORS
HAVE HUNDREDS OF
DIFFERENT WAYS OF
TREATING ILLNESSES
AND INJURIES.

BACTERIA AND VIRUSES

Bacteria and viruses are the most important causes of disease. Bacteria are simple plant-like organisms that can divide very quickly. They cause many common infections such as boils and acne.

Viruses are very much smaller, and technically they are not alive at all. They can take over an infected cell and turn it into a factory producing millions more viruses. They are responsible for many common diseases such as colds and influenza (flu).

QUICK FACTS

Viruses and bacteria are **CONTAGIOUS**, which means they spread between people in close contact with one another.

Scientists can only treat the **SYMPTOMS** of most viral infections, not the virus itself.

Not all bacteria are **HARMFUL** or disease-causing. Our bodies contain millions of bacteria that break down dead and waste materials.

When we catch a **COLD**, our immune system begins fighting it immediately. Colds usually last only a few days.

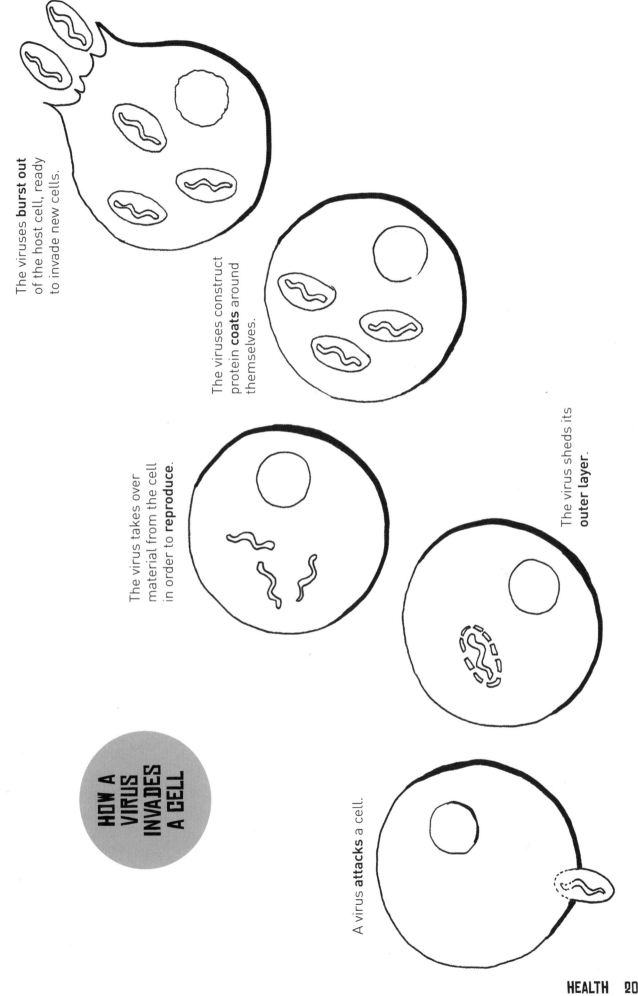

The viruses **burst out** of the host cell, ready to invade new cells.

The viruses construct protein **coats** around themselves.

The virus takes over material from the cell in order to **reproduce**.

The virus sheds its **outer layer**.

HOW A VIRUS INVADES A CELL

A virus **attacks** a cell.

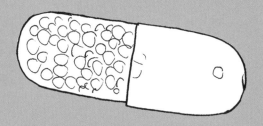

ANTIBIOTICS

Antibiotics are chemicals that help you to fight diseases caused by bacteria and fungi. Some are manufactured naturally by your body, but they are now made in labs, too.

Different antibiotics work in different ways: some stop bacteria reproducing, while others prevent them from absorbing nutrients.

QUICK FACTS

Antibiotics have **NO EFFECT** on viruses.

One antibiotic may act in different ways against different **GERMS**. It may kill the germs in one case, and in another only weaken them and let the body's natural defenses take over.

Drugs such as aspirin work by **PREVENTING** the sensation of pain from reaching the brain.

Today a lot of people are turning to **NATURAL** remedies rather than prescribed drugs. These are made from natural products like roots, plants, flowers, and trees.

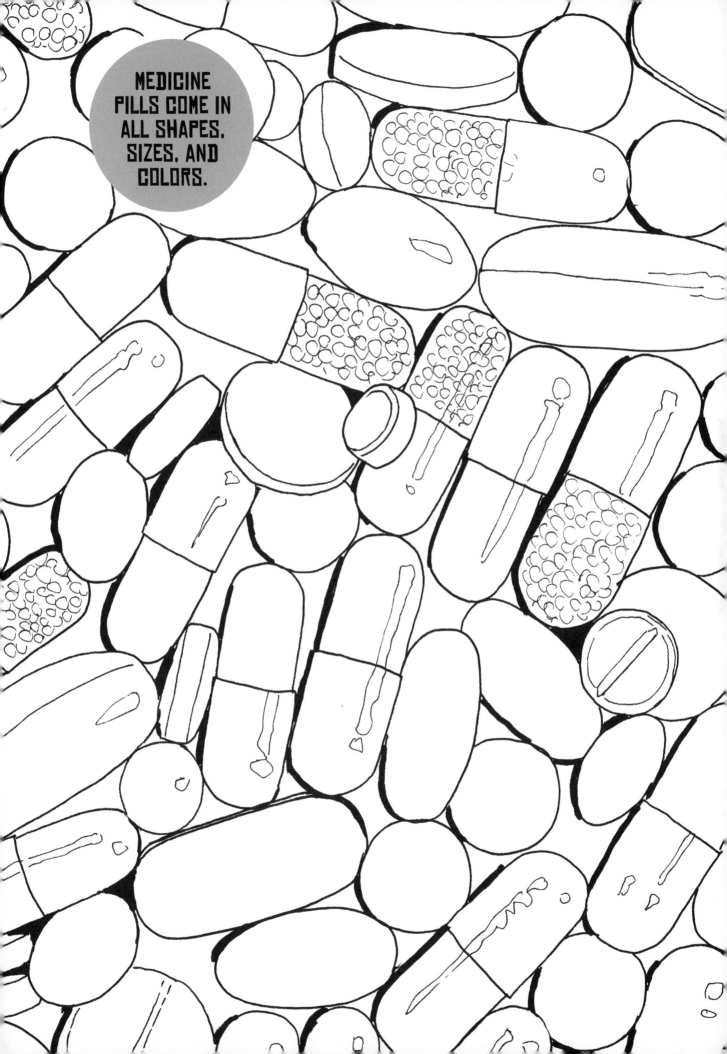

MEDICINE PILLS COME IN ALL SHAPES, SIZES, AND COLORS.

SURGERY

Modern surgery removes, repairs, or replaces damaged body parts.

When a doctor replaces a damaged organ with a healthy one from a donor, the operation is called a transplant. Nowadays the heart, liver, kidneys, and lungs can all be transplanted.

QUICK FACTS

The first successful **KIDNEY TRANSPLANT** took place in the USA in 1954.

The first successful **HEART TRANSPLANT** took place in South Africa in 1967. The patient lived for 18 days.

PLASTIC SURGERY involves grafting (moving) skin from one part of the body to another.

KEYHOLE SURGERY is performed through tiny incisions (cuts) in the skin.

Nowadays, surgical **ROBOTS** assist during some operations.

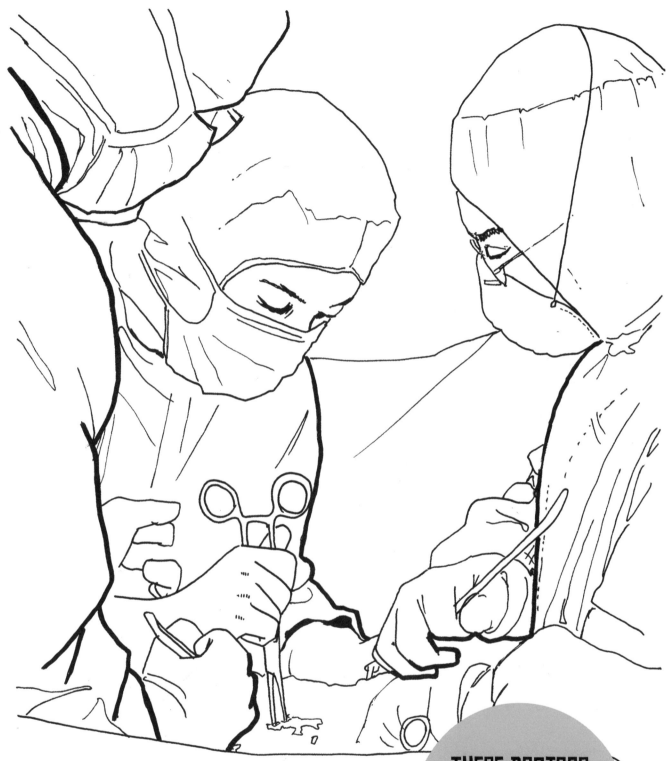

THESE DOCTORS ARE PERFORMING LIFE-SAVING SURGERY ON A PATIENT WHO HAS HAD A HEART ATTTACK.

COUGHS AND SNEEZES

Coughing is the way in which the lungs dislodge
anything that blocks the air passages.

When you cough, your vocal cords press together to seal off
your air passages. At the same time your chest muscles tense
up, raising the pressure in your lungs. When you release
the air it rushes out, carrying the obstruction with it.

QUICK FACTS

When we sneeze, a cloud of tiny water droplets is
EJECTED violently through the mouth and nose, carrying
with it any microbes present in your lungs. This is how
colds and influenza are spread.

A normal sneeze **TRAVELS** at about 10 ft per second.

The **FASTEST** sneeze on record blasted out at an
amazing 103 miles per hour!

It can be quite hard to breathe normally when you are
at the top of a mountain. At high **ALTITUDES** the air is
thinner so there is not so much oxygen in it.

Particles that have been irritating your nose and throat.

Saliva

Germs

Bacteria

Mucus

WHEN YOU SNEEZE, YOU SPRAY FLUID EVERYWHERE—MOSTLY OUT OF YOUR MOUTH, NOT YOUR NOSE.

LUNG HEALTH

Because our lungs must inhale the air from the environment, they take in bacteria, viruses, dust, and pollutants.

A sticky fluid called mucus lines the airways and traps most of these foreign substances, but many still get through, and can cause infections and ill health.

QUICK FACTS

SMOKING damages the natural cleaning mechanism of the lungs, and also poisons the cells that line the lungs.

Asthma is not a disease, but a symptom of some other condition. When a person suffers from **ASTHMA**, they find it hard to breathe.

Bronchitis is an **INFLAMATION** of all or part of the bronchi, through which air passes into the lungs.

In very polluted environments, wearing a **FACE MASK** can reduce the inhalation of potentially deadly particles.

A **BRONCHOSCOPE** is a hollow tube with a system of lights and mirrors, inserted through the patient's mouth into the throat and lungs. It is used to remove small tumors and pus, or take samples of lung tissue.

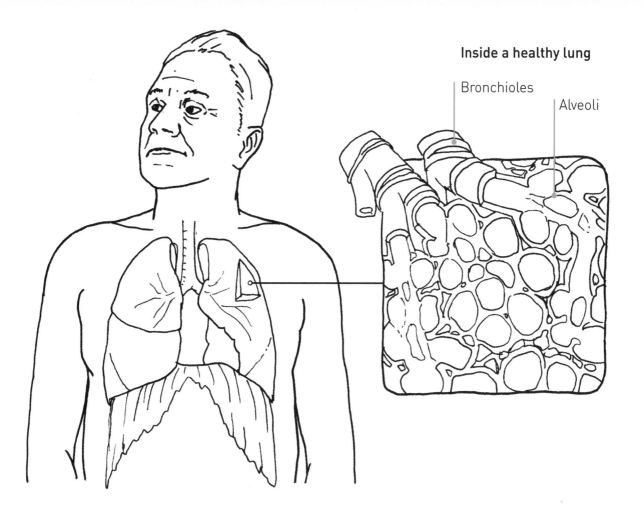

Inside a healthy lung

Bronchioles

Alveoli

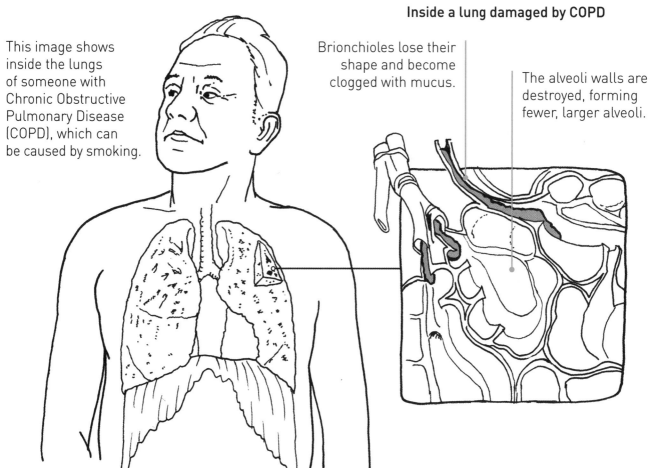

Inside a lung damaged by COPD

This image shows inside the lungs of someone with Chronic Obstructive Pulmonary Disease (COPD), which can be caused by smoking.

Brionchioles lose their shape and become clogged with mucus.

The alveoli walls are destroyed, forming fewer, larger alveoli.

ALLERGIES

An allergy is any condition in which a person reacts in a hyper sensitive or unusual manner to any substance. Allergic symptoms are the side effects of the reaction.

QUICK FACTS

In spring and early summer some people suffer from an allergic reaction to certain plants and pollens. This is called **HAY FEVER**.

The **RANGE** of allergies is very broad and people may react to various foods, drugs, dusts, pollens, fabrics, plants, bacteria, animals, heat, or sunlight.

Up to **EIGHT PER CENT** of children have a food allergy.

If a person develops asthma before they are 30 years old, it is usually the result of an **ALLERGY**.

Some people have very severe **nut** allergies, which can kill them.

Some people can't eat **dairy products** like milk and cheese.

LOTS OF DIFFERENT FOODS CAN CAUSE ALLERGIES.

It's also very common for people to be allergic to **fish**.

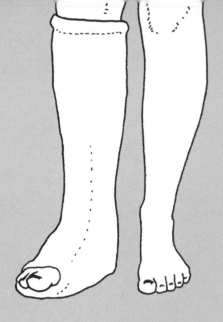

BROKEN BONES

When a bone is broken, the soft tissues around the break are torn and injured. Some of the injured tissue dies, and the whole area containing the bone-ends and the soft tissue is quickly bound together by clotted blood and lymph.

Mending a broken bone is somewhat like mending a broken saucer, except the doctor doesn't have to apply any glue. This is produced by the connective tissue cells of the bone itself.

QUICK FACTS

A **PLASTER CAST** is usually applied to a broken limb in order to keep the bone still and the broken edges in perfect alignment.

The ends of most bones are **CUSHIONED** by a pad of cartilage to protect them from impact.

An **X-RAY** passes through the soft parts of your body, to produce a kind of shadow picture that only shows your bones.

Bone tissue has an amazing ability to **REBUILD** itself.

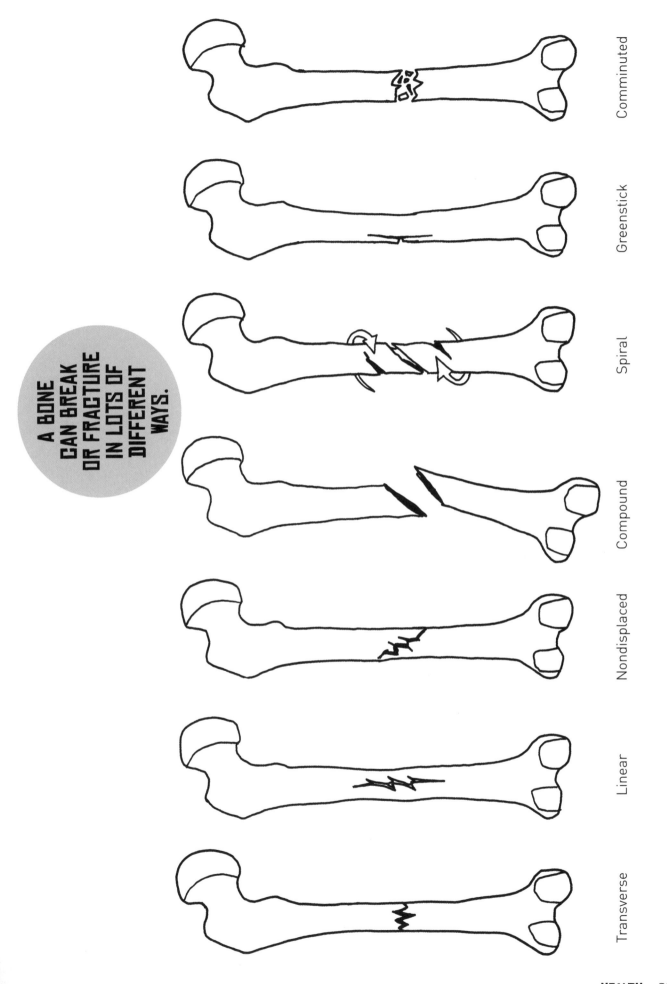

A BONE CAN BREAK OR FRACTURE IN LOTS OF DIFFERENT WAYS.

Comminuted

Greenstick

Spiral

Compound

Nondisplaced

Linear

Transverse

WEARING GLASSES

If your eye is not exactly the right shape, or the lens cannot focus properly, you cannot form a clear image on your retina. In this case you may need to wear glasses to correct your vision.

Glasses for shortsighted people have convex (inward-curving) lenses, and glasses for longsighted people have concave (outward-curving) lenses.

QUICK FACTS

As people get older, the lenses of their eyes grow harder and cannot change their shape to **FOCUS** close up.

CONTACT LENSES are an alternative to wearing glasses. They are made of very soft plastic that does not cause any discomfort.

However, some people find that putting them into their eyes is so **DIFFICULT** and uncomfortable that they prefer to stick to glasses.

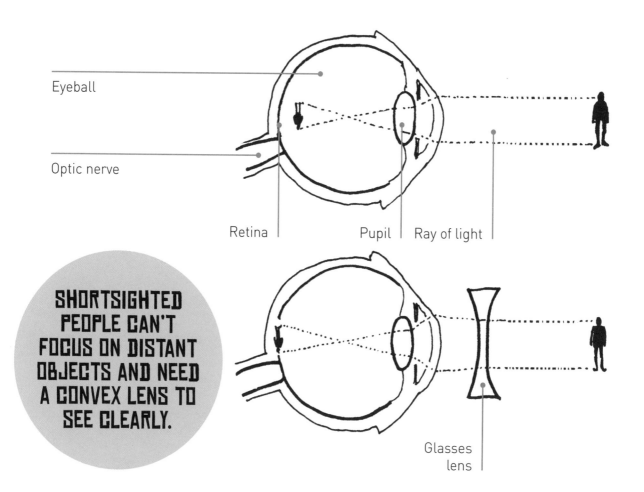

Eyeball

Optic nerve

Retina   Pupil   Ray of light

SHORTSIGHTED PEOPLE CAN'T FOCUS ON DISTANT OBJECTS AND NEED A CONVEX LENS TO SEE CLEARLY.

Glasses lens

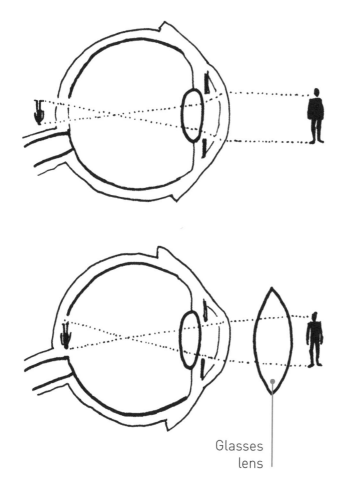

LONGSIGHTED PEOPLE CAN'T FOCUS ON NEARBY OBJECTS AND NEED A CONCAVE LENS TO SEE CLEARLY.

Glasses lens

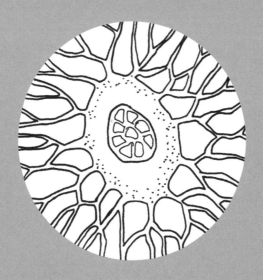

MICROSCOPES

The microscope is probably the single most useful
tool in the study of the human body.

It uses lenses of smooth-ground glass to magnify the images of
tiny objects. In this way, scientists can examine bacteria, blood
cells, and other tiny parts of the body, and study their behavior.

QUICK FACTS

A simple two-lens microscope was **INVENTED**
in about 1590.

Dutchman Antonie van Leeuwenhoek (1632–1723) made
a microscope with a tiny lens. He was the **FIRST** person
able to see bacteria, yeast, and living blood cells.

The English scientist Robert Hooke used an early
microscope to discover the existence of living cells
in **PLANTS**.

Some microscopes are so powerful they can magnify
the smallest objects many **THOUSANDS** of times.

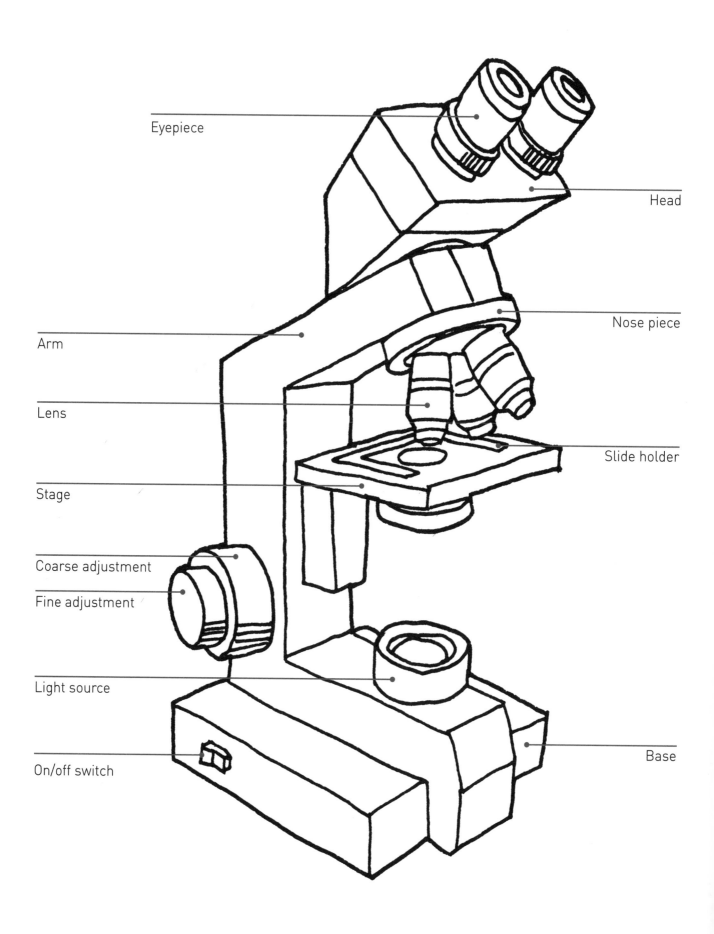

Eyepiece

Head

Arm

Nose piece

Lens

Slide holder

Stage

Coarse adjustment

Fine adjustment

Light source

Base

On/off switch

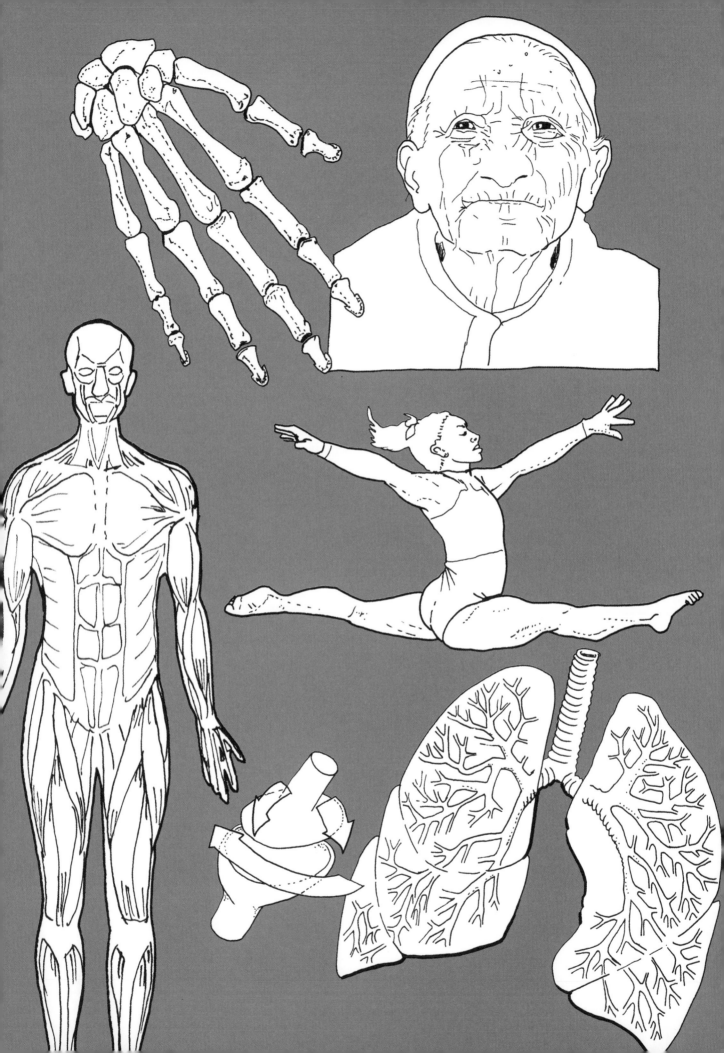

Look out for all three of the fantastic
Color + Learn titles:

Prehistoric World
Human Body
Science and Space

These amazing books all have over 200 pages
of facts and coloring fun!

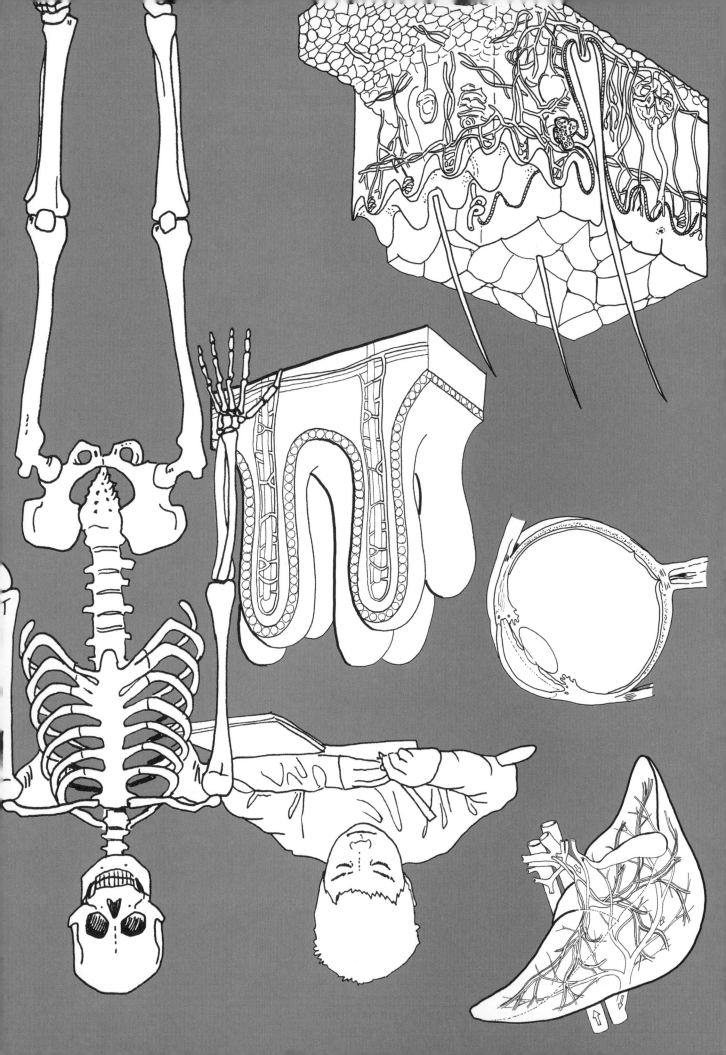